EXPLORING ALGEBRA

with

THE GEOMETER'S SKETCHPAD®

STEVEN CHANAN

ERIC BERGOFSKY

DAN BENNETT

Key Curriculum Press
Innovators in Mathematics Education

Contributing Authors	Daniel Scher and Nathalie Sinclair
Production Editors	Kristin Ferraioli and Jacqueline Gamble
Art and Design Coordinator	Caroline Ayres
Art Editor, Illustrator	Jason Luz
Copyeditor	Joan Saunders
Editorial Production Manager	Deborah Cogan
Production Director	Diana Jean Parks
Cover Designer	Ariana Grabec–Dingman
Cover Photo Credits	© Alec Pytlowany, Masterfile
Prepress and Printer	Data Reproductions
Publisher	Steven Rasmussen

Exploring Algebra Sketches CD-ROM

Key Curriculum Press guarantees that the Exploring Algebra Sketches CD-ROM that accompanies this book is free of defects in materials and workmanship. A defective CD-ROM will be replaced free of charge if returned within 90 days of the purchase date. After 90 days, there is a $10.00 replacement fee.

Key Curriculum Press
1150 65th Street
Emeryville, California 94608
510-595-7000
editorial@keypress.com
http://www.keypress.com

10 9 8 7 6 5 4 3   05 04 03   ISBN 1-55953-534-2

Contents

Chapter 3: Parabolas and Quadratic Equations

Chapter 4: Functions

Chapter 5: Transformations and Vectors

Activity Notes

Introduction

If names told the whole story, The Geometer's Sketchpad® would fill one simple purpose—to aid in the study of geometry. Sometimes, however, a software program outgrows its name. In the 11 years since its introduction, Sketchpad™ has matured and teachers have pushed its capabilities in unforeseen mathematical directions. With this book, the news is finally out: The Geometer's Sketchpad is a great tool for exploring algebra as well as geometry.

In some respects, this revelation shouldn't be surprising. Martin Gardner described the complementary nature of algebra and geometry as follows:

> There is no more effective aid in understanding certain algebraic identities than a good diagram. One should, of course, know how to manipulate algebraic symbols to obtain proofs, but in many cases a dull proof can be supplemented by a geometric analogue so simple and beautiful that the truth of a theorem is almost seen at a single glance. (*Knotted Doughnuts and Other Mathematical Entertainments* [New York: W. H. Freeman and Company, 1986], 192.)

Gardner's words were written before the explosion of technology into mathematics classrooms. In the mid-1980s, the graphing calculator became a bridge between the symbolism of algebraic equations and the visual nature of their accompanying graphs.

Version 4 of Sketchpad adds capabilities that extend those of a graphing calculator. You'll find numerous examples of interactive, "dynamic" graphs and equations throughout this book. But in assembling an algebra collection, we knew that Sketchpad could offer learning opportunities that the graphing calculator never could. Here are just some of the numerical and algebraic questions Sketchpad opens for study:

- What would it look like to model the distributive property of multiplication over addition with "virtual" algebra tiles?

- Is there a geometric way to compute the greatest common divisor of any two integers?

- How can square roots and irrational numbers be investigated on a Sketchpad grid?

- What properties of functions become more transparent when their graphs are displayed on a coordinate system whose x- and y-axes are parallel to each other?

- What algebraic/geometric properties of vectors can be deduced from an interactive Sketchpad model?

The activities in this book encompass much of the core content of a typical introductory algebra course—number properties, lines, graphs, functions, transformations, and polynomial factoring. Several more advanced topics are also introduced, including quadratics, linear programming, and vectors.

Each activity emphasizes visual, dynamic models. In many cases, students dive right into a ready-made sketch provided on the accompanying CD-ROM. At other times, they'll build a sketch from the ground up and gain valuable insights into the underpinnings of their algebraic model.

These activities are here for you to sample as a companion to your algebra text. They're ready for practically any occasion—for when you think a particular lesson is just right for exploration on the computer, for when your students start lobbying for a trip to the computer lab, and for that day when you just want to try something different. Even if you never leave your classroom, many of the sketches make great demonstration models to be viewed from a single computer and projector.

Whether you are a teacher or a student, we think the activities contained in this book will change the way you think about algebra. The Geometer's Sketchpad is likely to retain its name for the foreseeable future, but don't be surprised if you begin to think of it as The Mathematician's Sketchpad™!

Where Sketchpad Came From

The Geometer's Sketchpad was developed as part of the Visual Geometry Project, a National Science Foundation–funded project under the direction of Dr. Eugene Klotz at Swarthmore College and Dr. Doris Schattschneider at Moravian College in Pennsylvania. Sketchpad creator and programmer Nicholas Jackiw developed Sketchpad's first versions in an open, academic environment in which many teachers and other users provided design input. The openness with which Sketchpad was developed generated an incredible tide of feedback and enthusiasm for the program. By the time of its release by Key Curriculum Press in the spring of 1991, it had been used by hundreds of teachers, students, and other geometry lovers and was already the most talked about and awaited school mathematics software in recent memory.

Key Curriculum Press continues to study how the program can be most effectively used by schools. Funded in part by grants from the National Science Foundation, this research is reflected in these notes, in curriculum materials, and in the ongoing development of Sketchpad. By 1999, the *Teaching, Learning, and Computing* national teacher survey conducted by the University of California, Irvine, found that the nation's mathematics teachers rated Sketchpad the "most valuable software for students" by a large margin.

Using Exploring Algebra Activities

The Geometer's Sketchpad was originally designed for use in high school geometry classes. Testing has shown, though, that its ease of use makes it possible for younger students to use Sketchpad successfully, and the power of its features has made it attractive to teachers of college-level mathematics and teacher education courses. *Exploring Algebra* was designed primarily for first-year high school Algebra. Other curriculum modules available from Key Curriculum Press address the specific needs of younger and older students. You will find, however, that many of the activities here can be useful whether you teach middle school Algebra, Pre-algebra, Algebra 2, or college Algebra students.

Features of a Typical Activity

A typical activity has three main sections: an introduction that describes the objectives of the activity and provides some motivation and context; a section titled Sketch and Investigate, in which students follow construction steps and answer questions; and a section titled Explore More, which lists possible extensions of the investigation.

The questions in each activity range from short, fill-in-the-blank questions to those requiring full paragraph responses. Spaces for recording answers are provided on the activity worksheets, but in some cases, students may need a separate sheet of paper.

In non-introductory activities, construction steps are, for the most part, described in mathematical terms, not in terms of Sketchpad commands and actions. The directions are more concise, then, and allow students to focus on algebra instead of on details about using the software that become redundant as the students gain experience. For students who do need extra help using the software, hints appear in the margins. In some cases, further hints are included in the activity's Activity Notes (in the back of the book) in a subsection titled Construction Tips.

Explore More suggestions can be very challenging. Students who finish an activity early can get started on Explore More questions, but expect many of these questions to turn into long-term projects. You might occasionally want to prepare one of these questions to demonstrate as a class wrap-up. In addition to the Explore More suggestions that accompany individual activities, other suggestions are collected together as project ideas at the end of each chapter.

Activity Notes

Activity Notes are collected in the last chapter of the book and contain answers to the questions posed in the activities. They also offer more information about the particular audience for whom the activity is written, any prerequisite algebraic facts and terms the activity assumes, the degree of Sketchpad proficiency required, where students might encounter difficulty, how much class time to allow, and which sketches and custom tools accompany the activity on the CD-ROM.

The Activity Notes also serve as a home for all the good stuff that just couldn't fit into the main text. You'll find mathematical connections, interesting facts, and pedagogical insights into the structure of the activities.

Student Audience is specified as:

- *Pre-algebra/Algebra 1:* These activities are generally most appropriate for Pre-algebra students and as review activities for Algebra 1 students.

- *Algebra 1:* These activities are generally most appropriate for Algebra 1 students. Some may even be appropriate for advanced Pre-algebra students and as review activities for Algebra 2 students. Most of the book's activities fall into this category.

- *Algebra 1/Algebra 2:* These activities are generally most appropriate for advanced Algebra 1 students and Algebra 2 students.

Sketchpad Proficiency identifies one of three levels:

- *Beginner:* All the activities, including those designated *beginner*, assume the user's basic knowledge of how to use a computer in general and Sketchpad in particular: clicking and dragging, selecting, using menus (for constructing and measuring), and opening and closing documents. With activities marked *beginner*, students usually start with a pre-made sketch and often need little more Sketchpad proficiency than the ability to drag objects around and observe changes.

- *Intermediate:* In these activities, users are asked to do more actual Sketchpad work such as using the Toolbox and basic menu commands (especially those in the Display, Construct, and Transform menus). These activities aren't necessarily difficult, and detailed instructions are given for most steps. But novice users may find them too time-consuming. (Users might be considered intermediate after just a few sessions with the program.)

Advanced: These activities are for students who are fluent with the basics of Sketchpad and perhaps know several more advanced features as well. They can perform more complex constructions that may require precise mouse manipulations, advanced selection techniques, animation, and keyboard shortcuts. Students needn't be advanced to try an activity so designated, but they may find that it takes a long time or seems tedious because they lack the experience needed to do the activity efficiently.

How much **Activity Time** your students require on a particular activity depends largely on how much time you want them to spend writing about, talking about, and presenting their findings. None of the activities is designed to take longer than one 45-minute class period on the computer, but you might choose to spend a few days talking about one investigation. The class time suggested in these notes includes time to do the construction, manipulate it, make some observations, think, and write down one or more conjectures. It does not include time for extended discussion, presentations, or extensions of the activity.

Situating the Activities in a Classroom

To serve a wide variety of teaching and learning styles, the activities in this book are straightforward and consistent in presentation. However, the needs of each classroom are unique. As the teacher, only you know and understand the particular needs of your students. In this section, we offer suggestions for how to situate these activities—how to connect them to *your* students.

No matter how mathematically and pedagogically sound they may be, isolated supplemental activities often leave students feeling as though they must learn one specific skill or concept without seeing how it fits with what they know, what its importance is, or how it relates to their interests and experiences. *Situating* an activity means providing a sense of where and why certain concepts come up and why they have been chosen as important; it also gives students a chance to consider and question these choices. By situating the activities in relation to your classroom, you invite students into the process of doing—rather than just following—mathematics: noticing relationships, posing questions, considering alternatives, and communicating ideas.

Strategies for Situating Activities

Activity-situating techniques are useful at an activity's introduction to set the stage, during its unfolding to ground and direct its development, and on its completion both to recapitulate and to launch in new directions. When considering how to best situate an activity, try one or two of the following suggestions. (Of course, not all strategies apply to all activities.) Examples follow each suggestion, applying the strategy to one or more activities from this book.

1. **Setting the stage.** Connect upcoming topics to established or intuitive concepts, to other fields, or to other experiences. Something as simple as connecting new algebra ideas back to arithmetic and counting can help students make comparisons and find analogies between other areas of knowledge, gain surprising insights into ideas they "already knew," and become aware of a connecting structure underlying the mathematics they are learning.

   Thinking Differently: Again and Again. Before starting this activity, remind students that the basic process of counting—one, two, three— is iterative: It rests on the process of adding one to the previous result. Ask them whether they can imagine how this process of iteration could be used to describe the linear relationships they have been studying. The connections between a basic skill such as counting and a newly learned concept in algebra might surprise students but will also help them see how very similar ideas are used in a wide variety of mathematics.

   Squares and Square Roots. Students might wonder what this activity has to do with what they have been learning. Remind them that they know how to multiply, divide, and so on, but they have no straight-forward method for finding the square root. You might provide some historical introduction to square roots and to how irrational numbers were discovered. Most students find it strange that the decimal expansion of an irrational number goes on forever but that we can represent such a number with a finite segment. Voicing such responses gives students a connection to the strangeness and beauty of mathematics that have motivated mathematicians toward discovery for thousands of years.

2. **Inviting ideas.** Invite students to come up with their own methods for doing something before introducing the "book method." When students develop their own sense of the difficulties or constraints of a problem, they are more engaged and will be able to appreciate easier or more powerful methods that you, or other classmates, might offer.

   Reflecting Without the Reflect Command. See if students can come up with their own ideas about reflecting without the Reflect command. Suppose you had two points and you wanted to find the line of reflection that transformed one to the other—what could you do? Encourage experimentation. Students will develop conjectures about the relationship between the two points and the line, and will develop a sense that the line is in the "middle" of the two points.

Exploring Algebra with The Geometer's Sketchpad
© 2002 Key Curriculum Press

3. **Stretching the problem.** Encourage students to stretch their understanding of a situation by reframing it or examining its limiting cases. Look for alternate ways of representing the same problem, or consider changing one part of the question. Reinterpreting and reassessing a problem helps students better understand the core mathematics underlying the situation.

   Where Are the Giant Ants? This activity focuses on the transition from the first to the second dimension (how area changes with respect to length). But similar principles carry into the third dimension. Students could consider what would happen to volume when length or area changes. They might even conjecture about the fourth dimension. Such thought experiments demonstrate the power of analogical thinking in mathematics, connecting hypothetical ideas to concrete knowledge.

4. **Going backward.** Mathematics abounds with two-way processes such as adding and subtracting, simplifying and factoring, or differentiating and integrating. For some students, knowing how to undo something helps explain how to *do* it. Look for places where students can practice reverse-engineering a problem or mathematical idea.

   Translation/Rotation in the Coordinate Plane. In these activities, students learn to use vectors to transform one object to another. What transformation would bring the object back to its original position? How are the two transformations related?

5. **Asking "What if?"** These types of questions can help students notice different properties of a situation, and can also help launch them on their own investigations. "What if?" questioning is often used by mathematicians as they try to solve problems, and can include changing parameters, considering different shapes, and applying transformations.

   Equivalent Expressions: The Border Problem. Invite students to ask, What if the garden wasn't a square? How would the expressions change if we had a rectangle? This will both allow students to conduct a similar investigation with algebraic expressions, and show them that their findings relative to the square can extend to other types of shapes.

   Factoring Trinomials. Students are asked to factor only trinomials whose leading coefficients are square numbers. What if the leading coefficient isn't a square? Can you come up with examples that don't factor? Students will come to appreciate the conditions under which they can factor as well as the need for another method to deal with these "other" cases.

6. **Questioning the questions.** Students can often learn much about a concept by examining the *types* of questions they are being asked to solve. Questioning the questions can help make them seem less arbitrary to students and can also put students in the role of posing questions themselves.

   Points "Lining Up" in the Plane. Why are there so many questions? Do they seem similar in any way? Are any two pretty much identical? Which ones do you think could be discarded?

   Rotation in the Coordinate plane. Why do all the questions use angles that are multiples of 90 degrees? Can't you rotate with 45 degrees? Why would the author not have asked questions about such rotations?

7. **Discussing.** Moderate classroom discussions that allow students time to reflect on things, comment on them, and exchange views about what they understand. This is a good way of sharing insights and questions in the classroom and can lead to helpful disagreements and expose gaps in understanding.

   The Circumference Function. In this activity, the students build three different representations of π. Moderate a discussion with the following questions: Which representation is better? Which one will they most remember? Which two are most similar? Are there other objects in the mathematics like that?

   Functional Geometry. In this activity students are asked to conduct a series of investigations. Moderate a discussion about which of these investigations were most interesting, and why—were they surprising, obvious, insightful, . . . ?

You probably have other strategies to contribute to this list. By situating an activity firmly in the human context of your classroom, you'll both enlarge students' perspectives of the phenomena under investigation and help them see how different strategies and concepts relate. You'll also increase the activity's accessibility: Students with different strengths—those who are visually or kinesthetically oriented, those who need to see the whole picture before they can start building the parts, and those who prefer to proceed methodically—have a chance to engage in a problem. Most important, you'll honor students' interests and contributions and help them establish personal connections to mathematics, which in turn strengthens their motivation.

Exploring Algebra with The Geometer's Sketchpad
© 2002 Key Curriculum Press

Getting the Most from Written-Response Questions

Although some of the questions in these activities require simple answers from the students (a number or an equation, perhaps), many questions ask for more involved written responses. These questions attempt to guide students into expressing their ideas and hypotheses, reasoning about why certain things happen, and explaining their observations and conclusions. In short, they aim at the same goals as the NCTM Standards of Communication and Reasoning. Some students might resist such questions, particularly if they are accustomed to traditional textbook exercises. These questions might also present difficulties for those students whose written communication skills are weaker. Finally, these questions might also require more time and attention, resources which are at a premium in most mathematics classrooms.

How can you as a teacher encourage your students to engage in thoughtful writing? How can you reap the benefits of these questions without having to force every student to spend the required time and energy on each written response? This will depend on the particulars of your own classroom and students, but you might find the following suggestions helpful:

1. **Providing a why.** Students might ask why they have to "write out all this stuff" when they already "know the answer." Alternately, they might resist writing if they do not know the answer at all. In either case, you can encourage thoughtful writing by providing students with a good reason to do so.

   Mathematicians communicate with each other through writing for two reasons: (1) in order to provide clear and sometimes even enlightening explanations or arguments, and (2) in order to convince each other of the truth and coherence of an argument. Students might be more inclined to write thoughtfully if they are trying to come up with an explanation that can help enlighten a fellow student, or one that most clearly or succinctly explains something. A fruitful discussion might even ensue if students do not all agree on which explanation is the "best."

   Mathematicians, like other kinds of writers, also write in order to help them think through a problem. For students who claim not to know where to start on a written response, you can help by asking them to describe what they do know, what they can observe, and what they don't understand. This might initiate a student's reasoning process that will at least increase his or her own mathematical awareness, and possibly help answer the question.

2. **Providing a model.** Many students are uncomfortable with written responses because they do not know what is expected of them. One way to encourage thoughtful writing is to provide students with models of written responses. You might provide a question that is a variation of the one you would like the students to answer, and ask them to imitate the model response that you have provided. You might also provide a response to a question (students will find it surprising that their teacher is giving them the answer!) but one that has some flaws in it. Students can then be asked to critique the argument or to provide a better response. Either of these approaches will give students a better idea of what a good response looks like and will give them some practice with writing good responses.

3. **Talking it through.** Sometimes, it will be more appropriate to move from individual written responses to a larger group format where questions are discussed out loud. Students might benefit from working questions out in small groups, or even in a whole class discussion, since they will have to contend with other arguments or counter-arguments. One danger of larger group formats is that strong students might dominate the discussion and thereby leave weaker students lost; another danger is that of miscommunication—when students do not listen to each other. You can encourage the participation of more classroom members by focusing not exclusively on the book's questions, but also on relevant "meta-questions" such as: What was difficult about this question? Why did the book's author think this question was important? What question do you think would have been a better one? You can also help avoid miscommunication by asking students to write up each other's responses in their own words. Doing this with the responses of even one or two students in the classroom can sometimes be more effective than having students work on the questions on their own.

Using Sketchpad in Different Classroom Settings

Different schools have a variety of different classroom settings in which computers are used. Sketchpad was designed with this in mind, and its display features can be optimized for these different settings. Teaching strategies also need to be adapted to available resources. Here are some suggestions for using and teaching with Sketchpad in a classroom with one computer, one computer and a computer projection device, several computers, or in a computer lab.

Exploring Algebra with The Geometer's Sketchpad

A Classroom with One Computer

Perhaps the best use of a single computer is to have small groups of students take turns using it. Each group can investigate or confirm conjectures they have made while working at their desks or tables using standard tools such as paper and pencil or graphing calculators. In that case, each group would have an opportunity during a class period to use the computer for a short time. Alternatively, you can give each group a day on which to do an investigation on the computer while other groups are doing the same or different investigations at their desks. A single computer without a computer projection device or large-screen monitor has limited use as a demonstration tool. While preferences can be set in Sketchpad for any size or style of type, a large class will have difficulty seeing what's happening on a small computer screen.

A Classroom with One Computer and a Computer Projection Device

A variety of devices are available that plug into computers so that screen output can be displayed to a large group of people. These projection displays considerably increase your teaching strategy options. You or a student can act as a sort of emcee to an investigation, asking the class questions such as: What should we try next? Where should I construct a segment? Which objects should I reflect? What do you notice as I move this point? With a projection device, you and your students can prepare demonstrations, or students can make presentations of findings they have made using the computer or other means. Sketchpad becomes a "dynamic chalkboard" on which you or your students can draw more precise, more complex figures which can be distorted and transformed in an infinite variety of ways without having to erase and redraw. Watching you use Sketchpad as a demonstration tool is a good way for students to learn some fundamentals of the program before they go to the computer lab. You can also model good Sketchpad presentation techniques for students. Use large and bold text styles and thick lines to make text and figures clearly visible from all corners of a classroom.

A Classroom with Several Computers

If you can divide your class into groups of three or four students and give each group access to a computer, you can plan whole lessons around computer investigations. Be sure to:

- Introduce to the whole class what it is they're expected to do.
- Provide students with some kind of written explanation of the investigation or problem they're to work on. It's often useful for that explanation to be on a piece of paper which leaves students room to record some of their findings. For some open-ended explorations the

problem or question could simply be written on the chalkboard or typed into the sketch itself. Likewise, students' "written" work could be in the form of sketches with captions and comments.

- Make sure students understand that everybody in a group needs the chance to actually operate the computer.

- Make sure that the students in a group who are not actually operating the computer contribute to the group discussion and give input to the student operating the computer.

- Move among groups posing questions, giving help if needed, and keeping students on task.

- Summarize students' findings in a whole-class discussion to bring closure to the lesson.

A Computer Lab

Teachers using Sketchpad in the classroom often find that even if enough computers are available for students to work individually, it's perhaps best to have students work in pairs. Students learn best when they communicate about what they're learning, and students working together can better stimulate ideas and lend help to one another. If you do have students working at their own computers, encourage them to talk about what they're doing and to compare their findings with those of their nearest neighbor—they should peek over each other's shoulders. The suggestions above for students working in small groups apply to students working in pairs as well.

Exploring Algebra with The Geometer's Sketchpad
© 2002 Key Curriculum Press

Common Commands and Shortcuts

Below are some common Sketchpad actions used throughout this book. In time, these operations will become familiar, but at first you may want to keep this list by your side.

To create a new sketch

Choose **New Sketch** from the File menu.

To close a sketch

Choose **Close** from the File menu, or click in the close box in the upper-left (Mac) or upper-right (Windows) corner of the sketch.

To undo or redo a recent action

Choose **Undo** from the Edit menu. You can undo as many steps as you want, all the way back to the state your sketch was in when last opened. To redo, choose **Redo** from the Edit menu.

To deselect everything

Click in any blank area of your sketch with the **Arrow** tool or press Esc until objects deselect. Do this before making selections required for a command so that no extra objects are included. To deselect a single object while keeping all other objects selected, click on it with the **Arrow** tool.

To show or hide a label

Position the finger of the **Text** tool over the *object* and click. The hand will turn black when it's correctly positioned to show or hide a label.

To change a label

Position the finger of the **Text** tool over the *label* and double-click. The letter "A" will appear in the hand when it's correctly positioned.

To change an object's line width or color

Select the object and choose from the appropriate submenu in the Display menu.

To hide an object

Select the object and choose **Hide** from the Display menu.

To construct a segment's midpoint

Select the segment and choose **Midpoint** from the Construct menu.

To construct a parallel line

Select a straight object for the new line to be parallel to and a point for it to pass through. Then choose **Parallel Line** from the Construct menu.

To construct a perpendicular line

Select a straight object for the new line to be perpendicular to and a point for it to pass through. Then choose **Perpendicular Line** from the Construct menu.

To reflect a point (or other object)

Double-click the mirror (any straight object) or select it and choose **Mark Mirror**. Then select the point (or other object) and choose **Reflect** from the Transform menu.

To trace an object

Select the object and choose **Trace** from the Display menu. Do the same thing to toggle tracing off. To erase traces left by traced objects, choose **Erase Traces** from the Display menu.

To use the Calculator

Choose **Calculate** from the Measure menu. To enter a measurement into a calculation, click on the measurement itself in the sketch.

Keyboard Shortcuts

Command	Mac	Windows
Undo	⌘+Z	Ctrl+Z
Redo	⌘+R	Ctrl+R
Select All	⌘+A	Ctrl+A
Properties	⌘+?	Alt+?
Hide Objects	⌘+H	Ctrl+H
Show/Hide Labels	⌘+K	Ctrl+K
Trace Objects	⌘+T	Ctrl+T
Erase Traces	⌘+B	Ctrl+B

Command	Mac	Windows
Animate/Pause	⌘+`	Alt+`
Increase Speed	⌘+]	Alt+]
Decrease Speed	⌘+[	Alt+[
Midpoint	⌘+M	Ctrl+M
Intersection	⌘+I	Ctrl+I
Segment	⌘+L	Ctrl+L
Polygon Interior	⌘+P	Ctrl+P
Calculate	⌘+=	Alt+=

Action	Mac	Windows
Scroll drag	Option+ drag	Alt+drag
Display Context menu	Control+ click	Right-click
Navigate Toolbox	Shift+arrow keys	
Choose **Arrow**, Deselect objects, Stop animations, Erase traces	Esc (escape key)	
Move selected objects 1 pixel	←, ↑, →, ↓ keys (Hold down to move continuously)	

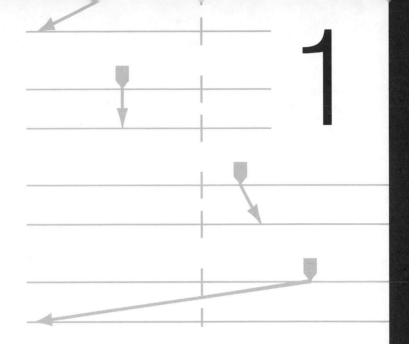

The Fundamentals
of Algebra

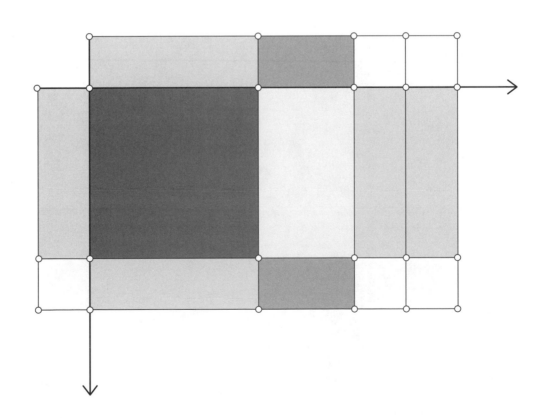

Adding Integers

Name(s): _____

They say that a picture is worth a thousand words. In the next two activities, you'll explore integer addition and subtraction using a visual Sketchpad model. Keeping this model in mind can help you visualize what these operations do and how they work.

Sketch and Investigate

Definition:
Integers are positive and negative whole numbers, including zero. On a number line, tick marks usually represent the integers.

1. Open the sketch **Add Integers.gsp** from the folder **1_Fundamentals**.

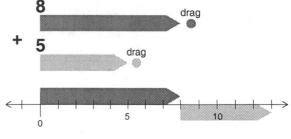

2. Study the problem that's modeled: $8 + 5 = 13$. Then drag the two "drag" circles to model other addition problems. Notice how the two upper arrows relate to the two lower arrows.

Q1 Model the problem $-6 + -3$. According to your sketch, what is the sum of -6 and -3?

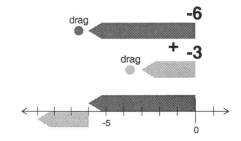

3. Model three more problems in which you add two negative numbers. Write your equations ("$-2 + -2 = -4$," for example) below.

Q2 How is adding two negative numbers similar to adding two positive numbers? How is it different?

Q3 Is it possible to add two negative numbers and get a positive sum? Explain.

Q4 Model the problem 5 + –5.
According to your sketch,
what is the sum of 5 and –5?

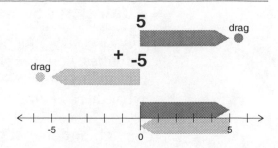

4. Model four more problems in which the sum is zero. Have the first number be positive in two problems and negative in two problems. Write your equations below.

Q5 What must be true about two numbers if their sum is zero?

Q6 Model the problem 4 + –7.
According to your sketch,
what is the sum of 4 and –7?

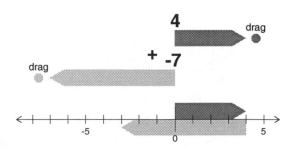

5. Model six more problems in which you add one positive and one negative number. Have the first number be positive in three problems and negative in three. Also, make sure that some problems have positive answers and others have negative answers. Write your equations below.

Q7 When adding a positive number and a negative number, how can you tell if the answer will be positive or negative?

Q8 A classmate says, "Adding a positive and a negative number seems more like subtracting." Explain what she means.

Q9 Fill in the blanks:

a. The sum of a positive number and a positive number is always a _____ number.

b. The sum of a negative number and a negative number is always a _____ number.

c. The sum of any number and _____ is always zero.

d. The sum of a negative number and a positive number is _____ if the positive number is larger and _____ if the negative number is larger. ("Larger" here means farther from zero.)

Explore More

To *commute* means to travel back and forth. The *Commutative Property of Addition* basically says that addends can *commute* across an addition sign without affecting the sum.

→ 1. The *Commutative Property of Addition* says that $a + b = b + a$ for any two numbers a and b. In other words, order doesn't matter in addition! Model two addition problems on your sketch's number line that demonstrate this property. Draw the two problems you used.

a. Given the way addition is represented in this activity, why does the Commutative Property of Addition make sense?

b. Does the Commutative Property of Addition work if one or both addends are negative? Give examples to support your answer.

Subtracting Integers

Name(s): _____

Once you understand how to add integers, you'll find that subtracting them isn't that much more difficult. You just have to remember one important thing:

Subtracting a number is the same as adding its opposite.

For example, 8 – 5 is the same as 8 + (–5). In other words, subtracting 5 is the same as adding the opposite of 5. This will become clearer as you work with an interactive Sketchpad sketch.

Sketch and Investigate

1. Open the sketch **Subtract Integers.gsp** from the folder **1_Fundamentals**.

2. Study the problem that's modeled: 8 – 5 = 3. Then drag the two "drag" circles to model other subtraction problems. Notice that the red arrow always represents the opposite of the green arrow. Notice also that the lower two arrows are being *added,* just as in the previous activity.

Q1 Explain how this sketch shows that "Subtracting a number is the same as adding its opposite." Use the graphic provided if you'd like.

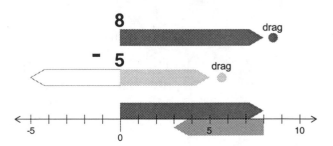

Q2 Model the problem 4 – 6. According to your sketch, what is the difference of 4 and 6?

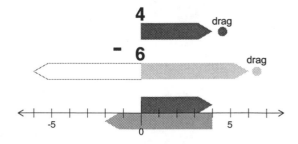

3. Model three more problems in which both numbers are positive but the difference is negative. Write your equations below.

Q3 When subtracting two positive numbers, what must be true if the difference is negative?

Q4 Model the problem −5 − 4. According to your sketch, what is the difference of −5 and 4?

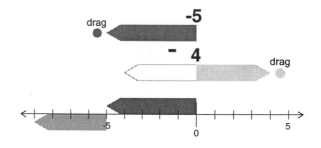

4. Model three more problems in which the first number is negative and the second number is positive. Write your equations below.

Q5 A classmate says, "Subtracting a positive number from a negative number seems more like adding." Explain what he means.

Q6 Model the problem 5 − (−4). According to your sketch, what is the difference of 5 and −4?

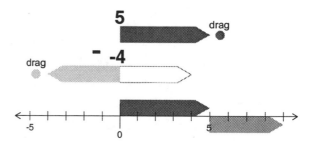

5. Model three more problems in which the first number is positive and the second number is negative. Write your equations below.

Q7 Model the problem –7 – (–4). According to your sketch, what is the difference of –7 and –4?

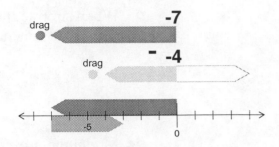

6. Model four more problems in which both numbers are negative. Have two answers turn out positive and two negative. Write your equations below.

Q8 A classmate says, "Subtracting a negative number is just like adding a positive number." Explain what she means.

Q9 When subtracting two negative numbers, how can you tell if the answer will be positive or negative?

Q10 You subtract two numbers (maybe positive, maybe negative) and get zero. What must be true about the numbers?

Explore More

1. In the previous activity (Adding Integers), you learned that the Commutative Property of Addition says that $a + b = b + a$ for any two numbers a and b. Model two subtraction problems that show there *is not* a commutative property of subtraction. Draw the two problems you used.

 Exploring Algebra with The Geometer's Sketchpad
© 2002 Key Curriculum Press

Multiple Models of Multiplication   Name(s): _____

What exactly *is* multiplication? There are many ways of answering this question because there are many ways of thinking about multiplication. In this activity, you'll look at three Sketchpad models of multiplication— Multiplication As Grouping, Multiplication As Area, and Multiplication As Scaling. You'll explore each model, then compare the three models focusing on how each "explains" multiplication by negatives.

Multiplication As Grouping

Perhaps the first way you learned about multiplication was in terms of grouping: 5 · 3 means five groups of three things. Here, we are grouping arrows of a particular length along a number line.

1. Open the sketch **Multiplication Models.gsp** from the folder **1_Fundamentals**.
   The sketch opens to the page Grouping.

Q1 "Put together three groups of 2" can be represented by the equation 3 · 2 = 6.

Model each of the following sentences on the Sketchpad number line. Then draw its bottom number line below, and write the equation for each sentence.

   a. Put together four groups of 2.

   b. Put together three groups of –3.

   c. Put together one group of –8.

   d. Take away two groups of 3.

   e. Take away one group of 5.

   f. Take away two groups of –3.

   g. Take away eight groups of –1.

Q2 Model the following sentences and write their equations. How are they similar and how are they different?

   a. Put together three groups of –4.

   b. Put together four groups of –3.

Q3 Using 4's and 3's, write and model two "take away" sentences whose product is the same as the product in Q2.

Multiplication As Area

Another way to represent multiplication is with the area of rectangles. In our model, the rectangle is in the *x-y* plane. Normally, the base and height of a rectangle are thought of as only being positive. But here, we'll say that the base is negative when *x* is negative, the height is negative when *y* is negative, and the area is negative when their product is negative.

2. Go to the Area page of the sketch by clicking on its tab at the bottom of the window.

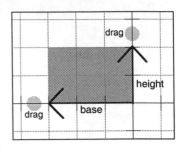

Q4 Study the problem that's modeled: $-3 \cdot 2 = -6$. Model seven other problems in which the area is -6 and write the equations below.

Q5 Model all of the problems in which the area equals 4 and write their equations below.

Q6 The numbers 1, 4, 9, 16, . . . are called "squares." Explain why this makes sense given the area model of multiplication.

Multiplication As Scaling

Whether you're "scaling" a recipe to serve more people or drawing a scale model of your room, you're using multiplication. This model is a little more complicated than the others, but once you understand it you'll see that it's also a very useful way to picture multiplication.

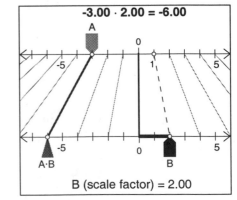

3. Go to the Scaling page of the sketch.

4. Study the problem that's modeled. The *scale factor*, *B*, is at 2, meaning that every number on the top axis *maps* (points) to a number twice as big on the bottom axis. *A* is at -3 and it maps to -6, so the equation for this problem is $-3 \cdot 2 = -6$.

Q7 Describe what the gray mapping segments look like for . . .

   a. a scale factor, B, of 1.

   b. a scale factor, B, of between 0 and 1.

   c. a negative scale factor, B.

Q8 Drag the scale factor B to the values listed below. In each case, drag A so that the product $A \cdot B$ equals 1. (For example, if B were 0.5, you would make $A = 2$ because $0.5 \cdot 2 = 1$.)

   a. $B = 4$; $A =$ b. $B = -0.5$; $A =$

   c. $B = -1$; $A =$ d. $B = -10$; $A =$

Q9 Make all of the numbers in Q8 fractions. What do you notice?

"Summing" Up

Q10 For each of the three multiplication models, list one strength of the model, perhaps something that it shows about multiplication better than the others.

Q11 Which of the three models do you think is most effective at showing *why* the product of two negatives is a positive. Defend your choice.

Explore More

1. The *Commutative Property of Multiplication* says that for any two numbers a and b, $a \cdot b = b \cdot a$. In other words, order doesn't matter in multiplication! Set up three pairs of multiplication problems, one for each model, that demonstrate this property. Draw these six problems on a separate page. Which of the three models do you think is most effective at showing *why* multiplication is commutative?

Raz's Magic Multiplying Machine

Name(s): _____

"Step right up, folks! Have I got a machine for you. You've seen number lines, right? I don't mind telling you, all those other number lines lack pizzazz . . . or, should I say, Raz-matazz?

"Say hello to our latest state-of-the-art number line. For starters, it multiplies. Give it any two numbers and it gives their product. Nifty, eh?

"But wait, there's more. I can show you things this number line does that will change the way you think about multiplication. They're not tricks, my friends, just consequences of multiplication itself. Care to give it a whirl?"

Static Multiplication

1. Open the sketch **Multiplying Machine.gsp** from the folder **1_Fundamentals**.

   Try dragging pointers A and B anywhere along the number line— pointer A·B automatically positions itself at the product of A and B.

You can use the right and left arrow keys on your keyboard to move a selected pointer one pixel at a time.

2. Drag A and B to represent the problem $3 \cdot 4 = 12$.

   The product, A·B, is to the right of the factors, A and B. This makes sense, since the product of two numbers greater than 1 is always bigger than either factor.

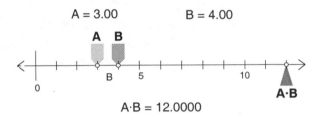

A = 3.00   B = 4.00

A·B = 12.0000

Q1 Drag A to 0.5 and B to 6. According to the machine, what is the value of the product $0.5 \cdot 6$?

Q2 List four pairs of locations for A and B such that $A \cdot B = 6$.

Q3 Find a location for A and B in which all three pointers lie directly on top of each other. Is there more than one location that works?

Q4 If B and $A \cdot B$ are the same distance away from 0, but on opposite sides, where must A be?

Q5 Can A, B, and $A \cdot B$ all lie to the left of 0? Explain.

Q6 Find locations for A and B to the right of 0 such that $A \cdot B$ is smaller than both A and B. Can you describe *all* locations for A and B for which this works?

Dynamic Multiplication

When you multiply two numbers on a calculator, the only interesting thing to see is the answer. Raz's machine gives the answer too, but in a much more visual way. As you drag A or B toward its intended value, you can observe the product, $A \cdot B$, as it moves simultaneously. Not only is this fun to watch, but it can deepen your understanding of multiplication.

3. Drag A to 0. Then slowly drag B back and forth along the number line.
   Notice that the product, $A \cdot B$, doesn't move at all—it remains at 0. This makes sense since the product of 0 and any other number is 0.

Q7 Drag *A* to 1. Then slowly drag *B* back and forth along the number line. Describe the movement of $A \cdot B$ in relation to *B*. Why does this behavior make sense?

Q8 Drag *A* to –1. Then slowly drag *B* back and forth along the number line. Describe the movement of $A \cdot B$ in relation to *B*. Why does this behavior make sense?

Q9 Drag *A* to 0.5. Then drag *B* back and forth along the number line. Which moves faster, *B* or $A \cdot B$? Explain why.

Q10 Find a location for point *A* such that the distance from $A \cdot B$ to 0 is always twice the distance from *B* to 0. Are there other answers?

Why Is a Negative Times a Negative a Positive?

Have you ever wondered why a negative number times a negative number is a positive number? Raz's machine provides a nice way to visualize the reason.

4. Move both *A* and *B* so that they're near the right edge of the sketch window. Now drag *A* slowly to the left, watching for $A \cdot B$ to glide across the screen.

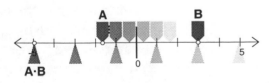

When $A \cdot B$ reaches the left edge of the sketch, move *A* in the opposite direction so that $A \cdot B$ glides back over to the right. Drag *A* back and forth for a little while observing $A \cdot B$.

This type of explanation is sometimes called "reasoning by continuity."

Q11 Based on what you've observed, explain why it makes sense that a positive number times a negative number equals a negative number.

Q12 Move B to the left of 0. Once again, drag A back and forth, observing the behavior of the product, $A \cdot B$. Based on the behavior you observe, explain why it makes sense that a negative number times a negative number equals a positive number.

Explore More

1. Open the sketch **Mystery Machines.gsp** from the folder **1_Fundamentals**. You'll see a multiplying machine with the numbers left off. Find the locations of 0 and 1 by experimenting with A and B. Mark your answers by clicking on the spots with the **Point** tool. Then press the *show answers* button to see how you did. Describe the strategies you used to find the locations of 0 and 1.

2. Go to the second page of **Mystery Machines.gsp**. This number line contains a single marked point—the number $\frac{1}{2}$. Find and mark the location of the number $\frac{1}{8}$. Again, describe your strategy clearly.

3. Go to the third page of **Mystery Machines.gsp**. This number line behaves differently. It takes two numbers, A and B, and computes their **sum**, $A + B$. Can you find 0 and 1? Explain.

4. Open the sketch **Mystery Combos.gsp** from the folder **1_Fundamentals**. This sketch contains three new machines. These machines take two numbers, A and B, and use them to compute a third number, C. For each machine, C is calculated as a unique combination of A and B. For instance, C might equal $A + B + 2$, or $B - A$, or $2A + B$, and so on.

   Hint: For each machine, place A on 0 and drag B. Then place B on 0 and drag A. Also see what happens if you place A on 1 and drag B, or place B on 1 and drag A.

   Investigate these machines by dragging pointers A and B and observing their effects on pointer C. Look for clues that will help you determine what rule is being used to calculate C.

Exploring the Properties of the
Four Arithmetic Operations

Name(s): _____

In this activity, you'll use Sketchpad "arithmetic machines" to explore the properties of the four fundamental arithmetic operations.

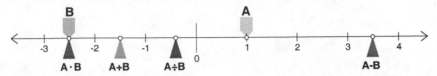

Sketch and Investigate

1. Open the sketch **Arithmetic Machines.gsp** from the folder **1_Fundamentals**. Play with the various "machines" on the five pages of the sketch until you're comfortable with how they work.

2. Make sure you have several copies of the "Arithmetic Properties Chart" found on page 17. Pick one of the descriptions, D1–D9, below. Following the instructions on the Chart, fill in the four cells— Addition, Subtraction, Multiplication, and Division—for that description. When you're done, try another description on a new Chart.

Here's an example of what the Addition cell might look like for D1:

Addition
a. A + B equals 0.
b. Yes, it's possible. A = 5 and B = −5, or A = −2 and B = 2, or A = 0 and B = 0.
c. Whenever two numbers are the opposite of each other (or both equal 0), their sum is 0.

The Descriptions

☐ stands for +, −, ·, or ÷.

D1 $A \square B$ equals 0.

D2 $A \square B$ equals 1.

D3 A, B, and $A \square B$ all sit at the same point.

D4 A and $A \square B$ move in unison, always pointing at each other, no matter where you drag A.

D5 A, B, and $A \square B$ are all to the right of 0.

D6 A, B, and $A \square B$ are all to the left of 0.

D7 $A \square B$ is to the right of both A and B.

D8 $A \square B$ is between A and B.

D9 $A \square B$ is to the left of both A and B.

Arithmetic Operations Chart

Name(s): _____

For each description D1–D9, complete steps a–c in each of the four cells below.

a. Copy the description, filling in the box (☐) with the appropriate operation (+, –, ·, or ÷).
b. State whether the description is possible. If it is, list three examples.
c. Write a general statement explaining when the description is true.

Addition	Subtraction
Multiplication	**Division**

Introducing the Coordinate Plane   Name(s): _____

As the story goes, philosopher and mathematician René Descartes was gazing upward, deep in thought, when he saw a fly walking on the ceiling. It occurred to Descartes that the fly's position on the ceiling could always be described by two numbers: its distance from each of two walls. Thus was born the *coordinate plane*, also called the *Cartesian coordinate system* after Descartes. In this activity, you'll investigate how to describe the locations of points in the coordinate plane.

Sketch and Investigate

1. Open a new sketch.

Choose **Preferences** *from the Edit menu. These are the default settings, so you may not have to change anything.*

2. On the Units panel of Preferences, change Distance Units to **cm** (centimeters). On the Color panel, uncheck Fade Traces Over Time.

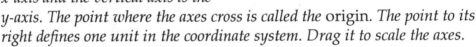

3. Choose **Show Grid** from the Graph menu.

   You'll see a pair of axes, a grid, and two points that control the axes. The horizontal axis is the x-axis and the vertical axis is the y-axis. The point where the axes cross is called the origin. *The point to its right defines one unit in the coordinate system. Drag it to scale the axes.*

4. Adjust your window, the origin, and the unit point so that –10 on the x-axis is at the left of your window and 10 is at the right.

5. Use the **Point** tool to draw a point anywhere in the sketch (except on an axis).

6. With the point selected, choose **Coordinates** from the Measure menu.

   The coordinates of the point form an ordered pair: two numbers that describe the point's location. The order of the two numbers is important!

If the point's label (A) isn't showing, click on the point with the **Text** *tool (the letter 'A' in the Toolbox).*

7. Use the **Arrow** tool to drag point A around, observing its coordinates.

8. Choose **Snap Points** from the Graph menu. Now drag point A around again. Be sure to drag it to the left and right of the y-axis and above and below the x-axis. Observe the coordinates and look for the relationship between these numbers and the point's position.

Q1 The first number in an ordered pair (x, y) is called the x-coordinate of the point, and the second number is called the y-coordinate. What do each of these numbers represent?

Q2 The x- and y-axes divide the plane into four regions called *quadrants,* numbered I, II, III, and IV. Using the following facts, label the four quadrants at right with the correct Roman numerals.

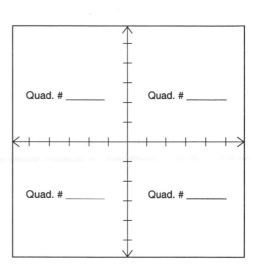

- In quadrant I, both coordinates are positive.
- In quadrant II, the x-coordinate is negative and the y-coordinate is positive.
- In quadrant III, both coordinates are negative.
- In quadrant IV, the x-coordinate is positive and the y-coordinate is negative.

Q3 For each problem, mark four locations satisfying the given conditions.

a. The x-coordinate of point A is equal to the y-coordinate.

b. The y-coordinate of point A is equal to 4.

c. The x-coordinate of point A is equal to –3.

a.

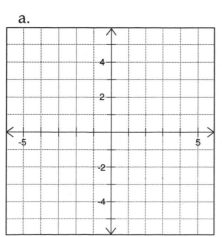

b.

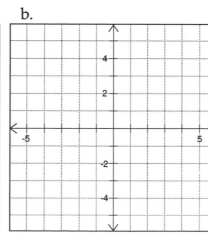

c.

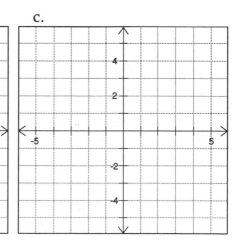

Q4 Find several different locations where the x-coordinate of point A is 0. Where must a point lie if its x-coordinate is 0?

Q5 Find several different locations where the y-coordinate of point A is 0. Where must a point lie if its y-coordinate is 0?

9. Draw a new point B and measure its coordinates.

Q6 For each problem, mark and label four pairs of points—A_1 and B_1 through A_4 and B_4—satisfying the given conditions.

   a. Points A and B have the same coordinates but in reverse order— for example, A: (2, 3) and B: (3, 2).

   b. Points A and B have the same x-coordinates, but the y-coordinates are opposites—for example, A: (2, 3) and B: (2, –3).

   c. Points A and B have the same y-coordinates, but the x-coordinates are opposites.

a.   b.   c.

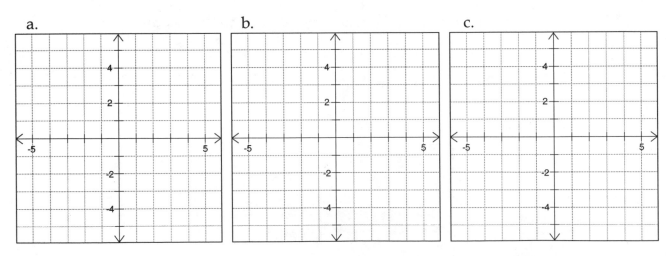

A Message

In the next several steps you'll move point A in the coordinate plane. If a meaningful message appears, you'll know that you correctly identified the locations of the coordinates.

10. Move point A to $(-3, 3)$. With this point still selected, choose **Trace Point** from the Display menu.

11. Choose **Snap Points** from the Graph menu to toggle it off.

12. Carefully move point A to the following coordinates, turning tracing off and on as directed. When you're done, the trace should spell something familiar.

> $(-6, 3)$, $(-6, -3)$, $(-3, -3)$, $(-3, 0)$, $(-4, 0)$, $(-2, 0)$, turn off tracing, $(3, 3)$, turn on tracing, $(0, 3)$, $(0, 0)$, $(3, 0)$, $(3, -3)$, $(0, -3)$, turn off tracing, $(5, -3)$, turn on tracing, $(5, 3)$, $(8, 3)$, $(8, 0)$, $(5, 0)$.

Explore More

1. List the coordinates of your initials, including instructions to turn tracing on and off, as in step 12. Then have a classmate test your list.

Equivalent Expressions:
The Border Problem

Name(s): _____

Suppose you want to build a square flower bed with a 1 m wide "border" to serve as a path. You need to know the area of the border so that you'll know how much gravel to buy. You haven't decided how big a square the flower bed should be, but you want to be able to find the border's area for any flower bed with side length *s*. You need an algebraic expression.

Equivalent expressions are expressions that look different but that give the same result, such as *x* − 2 and *x* + (−2).

Several different equivalent expressions are possible for this problem. Your goal is to come up with as many of them as you can and test them for equivalence by seeing if they all give the same area for any side length.

1. Open the sketch **Border.gsp** from the folder **1_Fundamentals**.

   You'll see a square with a border around it, representing the flower bed and the path. Eight quadrilateral interiors are constructed on the border—four green and four yellow. This arrangement represents one possible expression for the area of the border: 4s + 4.

Q1 Explain how the expression 4*s* + 4 relates to the quadrilaterals around the flower bed. Why does this expression give the area of the border?

If you can't see s's measurement in the sketch, drag the New Calculation dialog box by its title bar until you can.

2. Use the measurement for *s* (*s* = 4.00) and Sketchpad's Calculator to find the value of 4*s* + 4 for the current value of *s*. To do this, choose **Calculate** from the Measure menu. Then type 4, click on the measurement for *s* in the sketch, finish the expression, and click OK.

   Did you get the correct value for the area of the border? Drag the red point at the bottom-right corner of the flower bed. Is the calculation still correct?

Q2 Go to page 2 of the sketch. You'll see another arrangement of quadrilaterals around the border. What expression does this arrangement represent?

3. Repeat step 2 for your expression from Q2.

To construct a quadrilateral interior, select its four vertices and choose **Quadrilateral Interior** *from the Construct menu.*

4. Go to page 3 of the sketch.

   You'll see flower beds for the two previous arrangements, and many more with borders yet to be filled in.

5. On one of the "empty" flower beds, construct quadrilateral interiors in a new way to represent a different expression for the border area.

6. Use Sketchpad's Calculator to calculate the value of your expression for the current value of *s*. Does your expression work, even as you drag the red point to change the value of *s*?

7. Repeat steps 5 and 6 two more times.

Q3 Write your three new equivalent expressions from steps 5–7 below.

Explore More

1. Find as many more equivalent expressions as you can.

2. Plot the functions associated with all of your equivalent expressions. How do the plots demonstrate their equivalence?

   (For 4*s* + 4, for example, you would plot the function $f(x) = 4x + 4$. To do this, scroll up above all the flower beds and press the *Show Axes* button. Then choose **Plot New Function** from the Graph menu, type 4x+4, and click OK.)

3. Use properties of algebra to *prove* that all of your expressions are equivalent.

The Distributive Property: Diving In

Name(s): _____

Your neighborhood swimming pool is 30 ft wide. Its shallow end is 50 ft long and its deep end is 20 ft long. The pool's director needs to find the area of the pool so she can figure out how much a new cover will cost. She multiplies 30 by 50 to get 1500, and 30 by 20 to get 600. She then adds 1500 to 600 to get 2100 sq. ft. In other words, $30 \cdot 50 + 30 \cdot 20 = 1500 + 600 = 2100$.

Her assistant does the problem a different way. He adds the lengths of the deep and shallow ends, 50 and 20, to get 70 for the total length of the pool. He then multiplies 30 by 70 to get 2100 sq. ft. In other words: $30(50 + 20) = 30(70) = 2100$.

These two methods illustrate the *distributive property*—a property of algebra that explains certain types of equivalent expressions. In this example, the equivalent expressions are $30(50 + 20)$ and $30 \cdot 50 + 30 \cdot 20$.

In this activity, you'll experiment with a sketch that graphically illustrates the distributive property. Then you'll use "virtual" algebra tiles to investigate the distributive property further.

Sketch and Investigate

1. Open the sketch **Diving In.gsp** from the folder **1_Fundamentals**.

   You'll see a rectangle divided in two. Think of it as a model of a swimming pool with a shallow end and a deep end.

   | | b + c | |

2. Measure the lengths of segment *a*, segments *b* and *c* (along the bottom), and segment *b* + *c* (on top).

   *To measure the length of a segment, select it and choose **Length** from the Measure menu. Here, you can save time by selecting all four segments at once.*

3. Choose **Calculate** from the Measure menu to open Sketchpad's Calculator. Now calculate one of the two expressions for the area of the swimming pool. Click on the measurements in the sketch to enter them into the Calculator.

4. Calculate the other expression for the area of the swimming pool.

5. Drag any point to confirm that your expressions are equivalent for any values of *a*, *b*, and *c*.

Q1 Write your expressions as an equation. This equation is a symbolic statement of the *distributive property of multiplication over addition.*

_____ = _____

Virtual Tiles

In the next part of this activity, you'll use custom tools that construct virtual algebra tiles. With these tiles, you'll build models of distributive property expressions involving variables.

6. Go to the Tiles 1 page of **Diving In.gsp** by clicking on its tab at the bottom of the window.

   You'll see the equation 3(x + 2) = 3x + 6 modeled with algebra tiles. The blue rectangles represent x and the yellow squares represent 1.

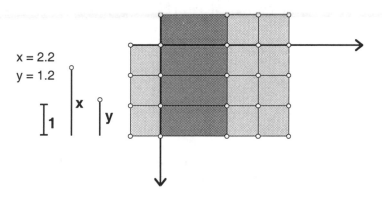

Q2 Which parts of the algebra tile model represent the *factored expression* 3(x + 2)? Which part represents the *expanded expression* 3x + 6?

7. Use Sketchpad's Calculator and the measurement for *x* to calculate the two expressions, confirming that they are indeed equivalent.

8. Adjust *x*'s slider (by dragging the point at its tip) to confirm that the expressions remain equivalent for different values of *x*.

9. Go to the Tiles 2 page of **Diving In.gsp**.

   You'll see an expanded expression, 4x + 4, modeled by eight individual tiles that form a rectangle "inside" the corner piece.

Press and hold the **Custom** tools icon to see the choice of tools. Choose the tool you wish to use, then click on a point in the sketch to construct that item.

Q3 Use the custom tools included with the sketch to build the length and width of the rectangle outside the corner piece. These dimensions represent the *factors* of the expression modeled inside the corner piece. Write the factored expression as the product of the length and width.

10. Calculate the expanded and factored expressions. Then adjust x's slider to confirm that the expressions are equivalent.

11. Go to the Tiles 3 page of **Diving In.gsp**.

    You'll see a factored expression, $y(y + 3)$, with the factors constructed outside the corner piece.

Q4 Use the custom tools to build a rectangle with these dimensions inside the corner piece. This rectangle represents the expanded expression. Write the expanded expression below.

12. Calculate the expanded and factored expressions. Then adjust y's slider to confirm that the expressions are equivalent.

Q5 Use the remaining pages in the sketch to expand or factor the following expressions.

Expand:

a. $3(2x + 1) =$ _____

c. $y(2y + 5) =$ _____

e. $x^2 + 7x =$ _____

Factor:

b. $3x(x + 2) =$ _____

d. $2y + 8 =$ _____

f. $3y^2 + 3y =$ _____

Q6 There are two different rectangles that can be built to model the expanded expression for f. above. Which of the two factored expressions do you think is more fully factored? Explain.

Explore More

1. Invent expressions to factor or expand. Include expressions with both x terms and y terms.

2. Does the distributive property apply to expressions with negatives or subtraction? How might you change the model to represent these expressions?

Expanding the Product of Two Binomials

Name(s): _____

Mono- and bi- are prefixes from the Greek words for one and two, respectively.

The expression $x + 3$ is called a *binomial* because it consists of two monomial terms: x and 3. The expression $(x + 3)(x + 5)$ is the product of two binomials. In this activity, you'll use Sketchpad algebra tiles to model expressions equivalent to the products of binomials. The process you'll learn, called *expanding*, is used for writing expressions in different forms and for demonstrating the equivalence of algebraic expressions.

Sketch and Investigate

1. Open the sketch **Binomials.gsp** from the folder **1_Fundamentals**.

   You'll see the factored expression $(x + 3)(x + 5)$ modeled with algebra tiles. The blue rectangles represent x and the yellow squares represent 1. Notice that one binomial factor is modeled vertically along the left of the corner piece and the other is modeled along the top.

   x = 2.7
   y = 1.6

Press and hold the **Custom** tools icon to see the choice of tools. Choose the tool you wish to use, then click on a point in the sketch to construct that item.

2. Use the custom tools included with the sketch to create a rectangle—made of smaller squares and rectangles—whose dimensions match those outside the corner piece. If you get stuck, go to page 2 of the sketch to see the solution.

   When you're done, adjust x's slider (by dragging the point at its tip) to make sure your rectangle holds together.

   The expression you modeled is $x^2 + 5x + 3x + 15$. You can combine the like terms to get $x^2 + 8x + 15$. This *trinomial* (expression with three monomial terms) is called the *expanded* form of $(x + 3)(x + 5)$.

Q1 Explain how each of the terms in the trinomial $x^2 + 8x + 15$ is related to the product of the binomials.

Choose **Calculate** from the Measure menu to open Sketchpad's Calculator. Click on x's measurement in the sketch and type from your keyboard to build the expressions.

3. Use Sketchpad's Calculator and the measurement for x to calculate the values of the expressions $(x + 3)(x + 5)$ and $x^2 + 8x + 15$ for the current value of x.

4. Adjust x's slider (by dragging the point at its tip) to confirm that the expressions remain equivalent for different values of x.

5. Go to page 3 of **Binomials.gsp**.

6. Use the custom tools to build the product $(y + 1)(y + 4)$ on the outside edges of the corner piece.

7. Use the custom tools to build a rectangle whose dimensions are $(y + 1)$ by $(y + 4)$ inside the corner piece.

Q2 Write the expanded expression represented by the rectangle. Be sure to combine like terms.

8. Use Sketchpad's Calculator and the measurement for y to calculate the values of the expression $(y + 1)(y + 4)$ and the expanded expression you just found. Adjust y's slider to confirm that these expressions are always equivalent.

Q3 Build and expand the following expressions on the remaining pages of the sketch. Draw the models in your notebook or portfolio.

a. $(x + 2)(x + 3)$ b. $(2y + 1)(y + 3)$ c. $(x + y)(x + 2)$

d. $(x + 2)(x + 2)$ e. $(2x + y)(x + 2y)$ f. $(3y + 1)(2y + 2)$

Explore More

1. Think of and experiment with ways the model can be altered to represent expressions with negatives. For example, how could you represent $(x + 2)(x - 3)$?

Factoring Trinomials

Name(s): _____

The expression $x^2 + 3x + 2$ is called a *trinomial* because it consists of three monomial terms: x^2, $3x$, and 2. Some trinomials can be written in *factored* form as the product of two binomials. In this activity, you'll use Sketchpad algebra tiles to model factored expressions equivalent to trinomials. The process you'll learn, called *factoring*, is used for writing algebraic expressions in different forms.

Sketch and Investigate

1. Open the sketch **Trinomials.gsp** from the folder **1_Fundamentals**.

   You'll see the trinomial $x^2 + 3x + 2$ modeled with algebra tiles arranged to form a rectangle. The dark blue square represents x^2, the light blue rectangles represent x, and the yellow squares represent 1.

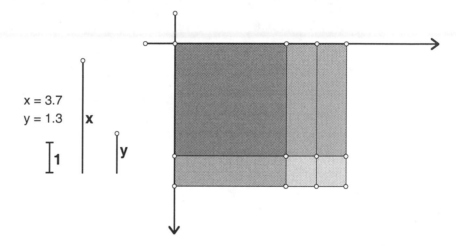

x = 3.7
y = 1.3

*Press and hold the **Custom** tools icon to see the choice of tools. Choose the tool you wish to use, then click on a point in the sketch to construct that item.*

2. Use the custom tools included with the sketch to build the length and width of this rectangle outside the corner piece.

   The dimensions of the rectangle are $(x + 1)$ and $(x + 2)$. This shows that the trinomial $x^2 + 3x + 2$ can be written in factored form as $(x + 1)(x + 2)$.

*Choose **Calculate** from the Measure menu to open Sketchpad's Calculator. Click on x's measurement in the sketch and type from your keyboard to build the expressions.*

3. Use Sketchpad's Calculator and the measurement for x to calculate the values of the expressions $(x + 1)(x + 2)$ and $x^2 + 3x + 2$ for the current value of x.

4. Adjust x's slider (by dragging the point at its tip) to confirm that the expressions remain equivalent for different values of x.

5. Go to page 2 of the sketch.

6. Use the custom tools to build a rectangle inside the corner piece to represent the trinomial $x^2 + 5x + 6$.

   Note: You need to use five x pieces, but it's not clear how many should be horizontal and how many vertical. Think of it as a puzzle—experiment until you get an arrangement in which the six unit squares fit to form a rectangle.

Q1 Build the rectangle's length and width outside the corner piece. Write the factored expression represented by these dimensions.

7. Use Sketchpad's Calculator and the measurement for x to calculate the values of the expression $x^2 + 5x + 6$ and the factored expression you just found. Adjust x's slider to confirm that these expressions are always equivalent.

Q2 Build and factor the following expressions on the remaining pages of the sketch. Draw the models in your notebook or portfolio.

a. $x^2 + 7x + 6$ b. $y^2 + 6y + 8$ c. $y^2 + 8y + 12$

d. $x^2 + 4xy + 4y^2$ e. $2x^2 + 3x + 1$ f. $4y^2 + 7y + 3$

Q3 Try to build and factor the expression $x^2 + 4x + 6$. Describe the problem you encounter.

Q4 Describe how the second and third terms of a factorable trinomial are related when the leading coefficient (the coefficient of the x^2 term) is 1.

Explore More

1. Is there more than one rectangle shape that can be made to model any of the factorable expressions in this activity? See if you can come up with a factorable expression for which more than one rectangle can be made.

Squares and Square Roots

Name(s): _____

Dot paper is essentially graph paper where the grid is made up of dots instead of intersecting lines. Dot paper is useful for exploring math and creating art.

In this activity, you'll use virtual Sketchpad dot paper to explore several interesting properties of squares and square roots.

Sketch and Investigate

1. Open the sketch **Squares.gsp** from the folder **1_Fundamentals**.

   You'll see a square constructed on a field of dots. Drag one of the two corner points to change the size and orientation of the square.

Select a side and choose **Length.** Then select the interior and choose **Area.** Both commands are in the Measure menu.

2. Measure the length of a side of the square. Then measure the square's area. Drag one of the points and watch the measurements change.

3. Calculate the square root of the area. To do this, choose **Calculate** from the Measure menu to open Sketchpad's Calculator. Then choose **sqrt** from the Functions pop-up menu, click on the area measurement in the sketch, enter a closed parenthesis, and click OK.

   What do you notice about the value of this calculation?

Q1 Fill in the blanks:

The area of a square is the _____ of its side length.

The side length of a square is the _____ of its area.

Q2 Given what you know about squares, why do the relationships in Q1 make sense?

Q3 Use your sketch to find the square roots of 12 whole numbers less than or equal to 20. Round all decimals to two places.

n:												
$\sqrt{n}$:												

Q4 Do you think it's possible to find the square root of any whole number using the method you used in Q3? Explain your reasoning.

Q5 There are many interesting number patterns to be found in this sketch. Here's one:

> Set up the square so that it's perfectly balanced on its tip—in other words, so its *vertices* are pointing up, down, right, and left. The smallest such square has an area of 2. The next biggest has an area of 8. We can think of this as a number sequence: 2, 8, . . .

Write down the first eight terms of this sequence. Then describe the numeric rule for the sequence.

Q6 When the square's base is horizontal, its side length is a whole number. But when the square is "slanted," its side length is usually an irrational number. In fact, you'll find only six slanted squares whose side lengths are whole numbers and that have at least one side completely within the sketch window. What are the side lengths of three such squares? (*Hint:* Think about *Pythagorean triples.*)

Explore More

1. In Q5 you looked at a number pattern involving the areas of squares as a vertex point is dragged diagonally. Find another number pattern that arises as you drag a vertex in a systematic way and see if you can discover a numeric rule for that pattern.

2. You may have noticed that even slanted squares have whole number areas. Write an argument explaining why. The figure at right may provide a hint.

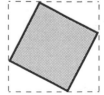

Chapter 1: The Fundamentals of Algebra
Project Ideas

The projects below extend your knowledge of the fundamentals of algebra and are suitable for in-class presentations, papers, or personal exploration.

1. Contrary to popular belief, monkeys are splendid mathematicians. Well, at least Consul the Educated Monkey is! Given any two numbers between 1 and 12, he can multiply them with ease. Open the sketch **Consul.gsp** in the folder **1_Fundamentals**. Follow the instructions to operate the multiplying monkey.

    Can you change the numbers on the sketch so that Consul can add any two numbers between 1 and 12? Can you extend Consul's capabilities in any other way? Can you construct a Sketchpad replica of Consul? (For some insight into Consul's amazing powers, consult the April 2000 issue of *Mathematics Teacher*.)

2. Somewhere in your mathematical upbringing, you've probably been asked to find the greatest common divisor (g.c.d.) of two numbers. The process is simple, but it's not particularly exciting. Would you believe there's a way to determine the g.c.d. by watching a ball ricochet off the sides of a pool table? Open the sketch **gcd.gsp** in the folder **1_Fundamentals** to try it out! Explain why this method works.

    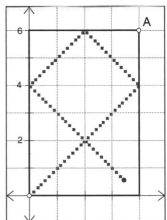

3. Two important techniques in algebra are *completing the square* and *factoring the difference of squares*. The sketches **Complete the Square.gsp** and **Difference of Squares.gsp** (from the folder **1_Fundamentals**) provide geometric models of these two processes. Learn about one or both the techniques and explore how the Sketchpad models work.

4. For a good introduction to algebraic expressions, open the sketch **Rectangle Areas.gsp** in the folder **1_Fundamentals**. Work through the pages of this document—instructions are provided there. Can you construct your own versions of these types of rectangles?

5. In the activity Squares and Square Roots, you saw that a square could have a whole number area and an irrational side length. This was known to ancient Greek mathematicians and was *extremely* upsetting to some of them. Why? Do some research on rational numbers, irrational numbers, and the *Pythagorean School* of ancient Greece. Present your findings in a report or a class presentation.

    For a greater challenge, research the proof that the square root of two is irrational and include your findings in your project.

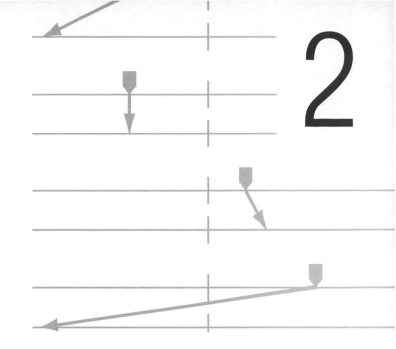

2

Slope and Lines

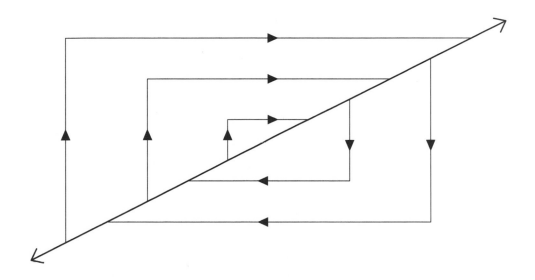

Points "Lining Up" in the Plane   Name(s): _____

If you've seen marching bands perform at football games, you've probably seen the following: The band members, wandering in seemingly random directions, suddenly spell a word or form a cool picture. Can these patterns be described mathematically? In this activity, you'll start to answer this question by exploring simple patterns of dots in the *x-y* plane.

Sketch and Investigate

1. Open a new sketch.

Holding down the Shift key keeps all five points selected. → 2. Choose the **Point** tool from the Toolbox. Then, while holding down the Shift key, click five times in different locations to construct five new points.

To measure the coordinates of selected points, choose **Coordinates** *from the Measure menu.* → 3. Measure the coordinates of the five selected points.

   A coordinate system appears and the coordinates of the five points are displayed.

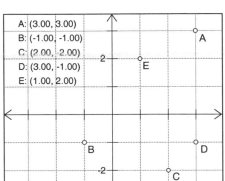

A: (3.00, 3.00)
B: (-1.00, -1.00)
C: (2.00, 2.00)
D: (3.00, -1.00)
E: (1.00, 2.00)

To hide objects, select them and choose **Hide** *from the Display menu.* → 4. Hide the points at (0, 0) and at (1, 0).

5. Choose **Snap Points** from the Graph menu.

   From now on, the points will only land on locations with integer coordinates.

Q1 For each problem, drag the five points to different locations that satisfy the given conditions. Then copy your solutions onto the grids on the next page.

For each point,

   a. the *y*-coordinate equals the *x*-coordinate.

   b. the *y*-coordinate is one greater than the *x*-coordinate.

   c. the *y*-coordinate is twice the *x*-coordinate.

   d. the *y*-coordinate is one greater than twice the *x*-coordinate.

   e. the *y*-coordinate is the opposite of the *x*-coordinate.

   f. the sum of the *x*- and *y*-coordinates is five.

The absolute value of a number is its "positive value." The absolute value of both 5 and –5 is 5. → g. the *y*-coordinate is the absolute value of the *x*-coordinate.

   h. the *y*-coordinate is the square of the *x*-coordinate.

a.

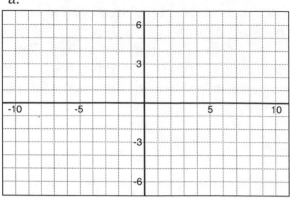

b.

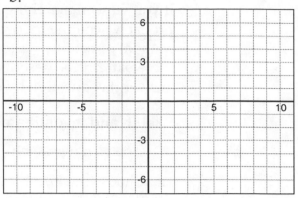

c.

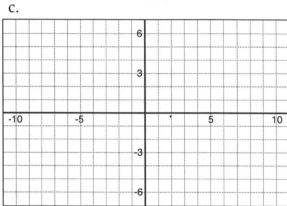

d.

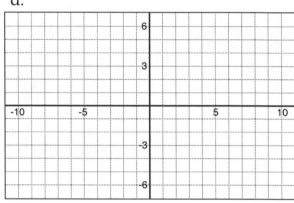

e.

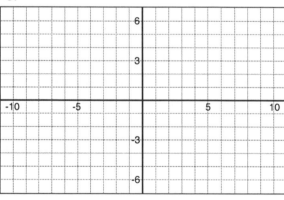

f.

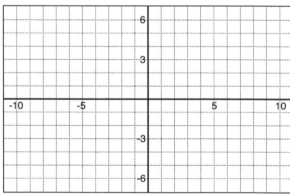

g.

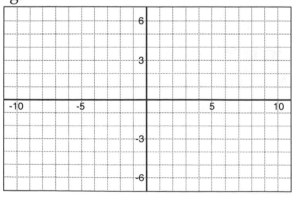

h.

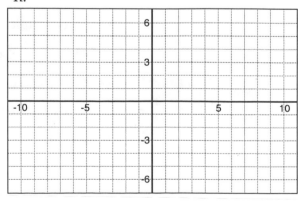

Backward Thinking

In Q1, you were given descriptions and asked to apply them to points. Here, we'll reverse the process and let you play detective.

6. Open the sketch **Line Up.gsp** from the folder **2_Lines**.

   You'll see a coordinate system with eight points (A through H), their coordinate measurements, and eight action buttons.

Q2 For each letter, press the corresponding button in the sketch. Like the members of a marching band, the points will "wander" until they form a pattern. Study the coordinates of the points in each pattern, then write a description (like the ones in Q1) for each one.

   a.

   b.

   c.

   d.

   e.

   f.

   g.

   h.

Explore More

1. Each of the "descriptions" in this activity can be written as an equation. For example, part b of Q1 ("the y-coordinate is one greater than the x-coordinate") can be written as $y = x + 1$. Write an equation for each description in Q1 and Q2.

2. Add your own action buttons to those in **Line Up.gsp**, then see if your classmates can come up with descriptions or equations for your patterns. Instructions on how to do this are on page 2 of the sketch.

The Slope of a Line

Name(s): _____

The *steepness* of things—ski runs, wheelchair ramps, or lines in the *x-y* plane—can be described in lots of ways. Skiers know that "black diamond" runs are challenging and steep, whereas "green circle" runs are easier and less steep. Mathematicians prefer to use *numbers* so that they can compare the steepness of objects and solve problems. In this activity, you'll explore a mathematical description of a line's steepness: the *slope*.

Sketch and Investigate

1. Open a new sketch.

2. Using the **Line** tool, draw a line.

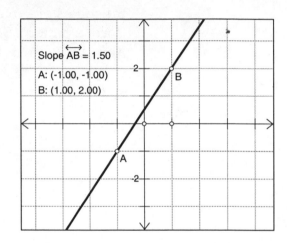
Slope $\overleftrightarrow{AB}$ = 1.50
A: (-1.00, -1.00)
B: (1.00, 2.00)

*If the **Line** tool isn't showing, press down on the current **Straightedge** tool and choose the **Line** tool from the palette that pops up.*

3. With the line still selected, measure its slope by choosing **Slope** from the Measure menu.

*Deselect all objects by clicking in blank space with the **Arrow** tool. Then select the two points and choose **Coordinates** from the Measure menu.*

4. Measure the coordinates of the two points defining the line.

5. If the points' labels aren't showing, display them by clicking on the points with the **Text** tool (the letter 'A' in the Toolbox).

6. Choose **Snap Points** from the Graph menu.
   From now on, points will only move to locations with integer coordinates when dragged.

7. Drag *A* and *B* to different locations and observe the changes in the slope measurements of the line.

Q1 Describe lines that have the following slopes:

   a. a slope of 1

   b. a slope of –1

   c. a slope of 0

   d. an undefined slope

   e. any positive slope

   f. any negative slope

Q2 How do lines with a slope greater than 1 compare to lines with a slope of 1? How do lines with a slope between 0 and 1 compare to lines with a slope of 1?

Q3 How do lines having a particular slope (positive or negative) compare to lines having the opposite slope?

Be sure to drag the line itself and not either of its control points. → **Q4** How does a line move when it's dragged with the **Arrow** tool? What happens to the slope measurement when a line is dragged this way?

Q5 Fill in the following table. (Move point A to the indicated location; then find the coordinates of at least two locations for point B that make the slope of $\overleftrightarrow{AB}$ equal the value in the left column.)

"Coord's" is short for "Coordinates." →

Make your sketch window as big as possible. You still may need to scroll or do your own calculations to find two answers to some of these problems.

Slope	Coord's of A	Coord's of B	Other Coord's of B
a. 2.000	(0, 0)		
b. –3.000	(2, 3)		
c. 0.000	(–1, 4)		
d. 1.250	(2, –5)		
e. Undefined	(3, 1)		
f. –2.667	(–1, –3)		
g. 0.125	(–3, 2)		
h. 3.500	(4, 2)		

Explore More

1. Mathematicians use *slope* to describe the steepness of lines. Skiers use colored shapes—such as black diamonds and green circles—to rate the steepness of ski runs. Can you think of other kinds of descriptions people use for the steepness of similar things?

The Slope Game

Name(s): _____

Imagine a game that combines the best elements of laser tag, Doom, and chess. This is not that game. But it is a pretty fun math game that's good for solidifying your sense of slope. The game works best with a partner (this is how it's described), but you can also play it alone if you cover your eyes or part of the screen at the appropriate moments.

If the **Line** tool isn't showing, press down on the current **Straightedge** tool and choose the **Line** tool from the palette that pops up.

Playing the Slope Game

1. Open a new sketch.

→ 2. Using the **Line** tool, draw five different random lines in your sketch. Make sure their labels aren't showing.

An easy way to select all five lines is to choose the **Line** tool, then choose **Select All Lines** from the Edit menu.

→ 3. Measure the slopes of the five lines by selecting them and choosing **Slope** from the Measure menu.

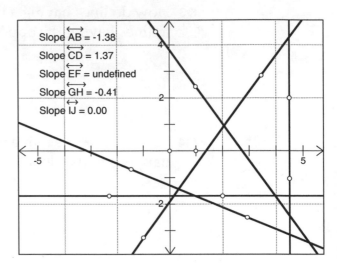

Slope $\overleftrightarrow{AB}$ = -1.38
Slope $\overleftrightarrow{CD}$ = 1.37
Slope $\overleftrightarrow{EF}$ = undefined
Slope $\overleftrightarrow{GH}$ = -0.41
Slope $\overleftrightarrow{IJ}$ = 0.00

4. Challenge your partner to match each measured slope with a line. Your partner is only allowed to drag measurements—to move them next to the lines they match. The lines and points are "off limits" until all measurements have been matched with lines.

With the **Point** tool active, choose **Select All Points** from the Edit menu. Then choose **Show Labels** from the Display menu.

→ 5. To check how your partner scored, show all the point labels. Award one point for each correctly matched slope.

6. Switch roles, scramble the lines, and play the game again. After a round or two, add and measure several more lines to make the game more challenging.

You can use the space below to record your scores.

How Slope Is Measured

Name(s): _____

When building a way to get from the first to the second floor, contractors usually don't build a ramp—they build stairs. How steep the stairs are depends on the *rise* (height) and *run* (depth) of each step. Tall steps with very little depth make for very steep (and dangerous!) stairs. Short steps with a lot of depth make for very "gentle" stairs. As you'll see, this way of describing steepness is closely related to how *slope* is defined in math.

In carpentry, the vertical part of a step is sometimes called the riser and the horizontal part the tread.

Sketch and Investigate

1. Open the sketch **Rise Run.gsp** from the folder **2_Lines**.

The rise is like the height of a stair and the run is like the depth.

   Segment "rise" represents a vertical path straight up or down from point A. Segment "run" represents a horizontal path right or left to point B.

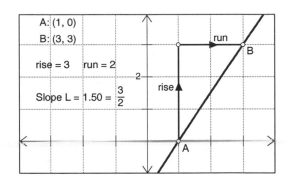

Q1 For each row, drag *A* and *B* to match the given conditions and fill in the rest of the row. (The first row has been filled in for you.)

point A: (x_A, y_A)	point B: (x_B, y_B)	run	rise	slope of L
(2 , 1)	(4, 2)	2	1	0.5
(4, 0)	(5, 3)			
(−5, −1)	(−3, 4)			
(−5, 3)	(5, 4)			
(2, −3)	(,)	2	6	

Q2 In Q1, point *B* was always above and to the right of point *A* and the rise and run were always positive. What happens if *B* is below or to the left of *A*? Fill in the following table to find out.

point A: (x_A, y_A)	point B: (x_B, y_B)	run	rise	slope of L
(2, 1)	(4, 0)			
(1, −1)	(0, 4)			
(−3, 6)	(−5, −1)			
(3, 5)	(,)	−4	−3	

Q3 Fill in the following table with three different locations for point B that each result in the same slope.

point A: (x_A, y_A)	point B: (x_B, y_B)	run	rise	slope of L
(2, 1)	(4, 2)	2	1	0.5
(2, 1)	(,)			0.5
(2, 1)	(,)			0.5
(2, 1)	(,)			0.5

Q4 Looking back at your tables, you should notice a relationship between *rise, run,* and the slope of L. Write a formula for *slope* that uses *rise* and *run.*

slope =

Q5 There is a simple formula for *rise* that uses some or all of x_A, y_A, x_B, and y_B. What is that formula?

rise =

Q6 There is an equally simple formula for *run* that uses some or all of x_A, y_A, x_B, and y_B. What is that formula?

run =

Q7 Now, use your equations from Q5 and Q6 to rewrite your *slope* equation using x_A, y_A, x_B, and y_B.

slope =

Explore More

1. So far, you've thought of *rise* as going up or down from point A and *run* as going right or left from there to point B. Would the slope be different if you went the other way? Press the button *Show B to A*. You'll see a new segment, *RISE*, that goes up or down from point B, and *RUN*, that goes left or right from there back to A. Explain why the slope is the same regardless of whether you go from A to B along *rise* and *run* or from B to A along *RISE* and *RUN*.

2. In the activity The Slope of a Line, you learned that the slope of any horizontal line is 0 and the slope of any vertical line is undefined. Explain why this makes sense now that you know how slope is measured.

Slopes of Parallel and Perpendicular Lines

Name(s): _____

It's often important to know whether two lines are parallel or perpendicular. Are there straightforward ways of figuring this out? In this activity, you'll find out.

Sketch and Investigate

1. Open a new sketch.

2. Choose **Preferences** from the Edit menu. On the Units panel, set Angle Precision to **hundredths** and Scalar Precision to **thousandths**. On the Text panel, make sure For All New Points is checked.

With both lines selected, choose **Intersection** *from the Construct menu. Or, just click on the spot with the* **Arrow** *tool.*

3. Using the **Line** tool, draw lines AB and CD. Then construct their point of intersection, E.

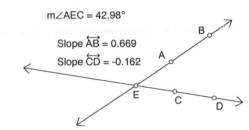

$m\angle AEC = 42.98°$

Slope $\overleftrightarrow{AB} = 0.669$

Slope $\overleftrightarrow{CD} = -0.162$

Select, in order, points A, E, and C; then choose **Angle** *from the Measure menu.*

4. Measure $\angle AEC$.

5. Measure the slopes of $\overleftrightarrow{AB}$ and $\overleftrightarrow{CD}$ by selecting them and choosing **Slope** from the Measure menu.

   A coordinate system and the slope measurement appear.

6. Drag various objects in the sketch and observe the measurements.

Q1 Make the slopes as close to equal as you can. What do you observe about the measure of the angle between the lines?

Q2 What can you say about lines with equal slopes? How could you verify this conjecture?

Choose **Calculate** *from the Measure menu to open the Calculator. Click on a measurement in the sketch to enter it into a calculation.*

7. Calculate the product of the slopes of $\overleftrightarrow{AB}$ and $\overleftrightarrow{CD}$.

Q3 Drag various objects and observe the product measurement. What does this value tell about the two lines? Do any particular values seem to have special importance?

Q4 Make sure that neither line is horizontal. Now drag points to make m∠AEC as close to 90° as you can. What does the product of the slopes of perpendicular lines appear to be?

Q5 Why is the product in Q4 always negative?

Q6 The product of the slopes of two lines is undefined if one of the lines is vertical. Why is this?

Explore More

1. Mathematicians—and math students—should be *skeptical*; that is, they shouldn't believe things based on little evidence. To be more confident of your conjecture about perpendicular lines, construct perpendicular lines using the **Perpendicular Line** command in the Construct menu and then make the necessary measurements and calculations. Is this more convincing than what you did before? Have you *proved* your conjecture?

A *vector* consists of a distance and a direction, such as *30 ft to the right*. The vector from point *A* to point *B* can be thought of as the distance and direction one would have to go to get from point *A* to point *B*.

2. Try the following: Select points *A* and *B* and choose **Mark Vector** from the Transform menu. Select point *C* and choose **Translate** from the Transform menu; click OK to translate by the marked vector. Now select the new point (*C'*) and point *D* and choose **Merge Points** from the Edit menu. The two lines now have the exact same slope *and the angle measurement disappears*. Why do you think this happens?

3. Explain why saying that the product of the slopes of perpendicular lines is –1 is the same as saying that the slopes are *opposite reciprocals* of each other. (Look up the work *reciprocal* if necessary.)

Direct Variation   Name(s): _____

What happens to the area of a parallelogram if you keep the length of the base constant while varying the height? (Try to answer this question before reading on . . .) The answer relates to an important type of function in algebra called *direct variation*. In this activity, you'll learn what direct variation is and how it's represented symbolically and graphically.

Sketch

You'll start by constructing a parallelogram and its interior.

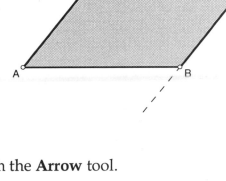

1. In a new sketch, construct $\overline{AB}$ and $\overline{AC}$.

Select point *C* and segment *AB* and choose **Parallel Line** from the Construct menu.

2. Construct a line through point *C*, parallel to $\overline{AB}$.

3. Construct a line through point *B*, parallel to $\overline{AC}$.

4. Construct point *D* at the intersection of the two new lines by clicking on this spot with the **Arrow** tool.

5. Hide the lines and construct $\overline{BD}$ and $\overline{CD}$.

   You've constructed a parallelogram. Drag different parts of it to be sure it holds together.

Select the four points clockwise or counterclockwise and choose **Quadrilateral Interior** from the Construct menu.

6. Construct polygon interior *ABDC*.

Now you'll take some measurements and explore them by graphing.

7. Measure the area of the interior by selecting it and choosing **Area** from the Measure menu.

To change a measurement's label, double-click it with the **Text** tool.

8. Measure the length of base *AB* using the **Length** command in the Measure menu. Change the label of this measurement to *b* for base.

9. Measure the distance from point *C* to $\overline{AB}$. (Select these two objects and choose **Distance** from the Measure menu.) Change the label of this measurement to *h* for height.

10. Select, in order, the height and area measurements and choose **Plot As (x, y)** from the Graph menu.

    A point is plotted whose x- and y-coordinates are the height and area of the parallelogram, respectively. If you can't see it yet, you will soon.

To trace an object, select it and choose **Trace** from the Display menu. Do the same to toggle tracing off. To clear traces from the screen, choose **Erase Traces** from the Display menu.

11. Drag point *C* closer to $\overline{AB}$ and observe the effect on the plotted point. Trace the plotted point so you can better see what it does as you drag point *C* around the sketch plane.

Direct Variation (continued)

Investigate

Q1 What does the path of the plotted point tell you about how height and area relate in a parallelogram whose base is held constant?

You may remember this formula from a previous course. If not, try this: Choose **Snap Points** from the Graph menu; then drag points *A*, *B*, and *C* so that you get whole numbers for base, height, and area.

Q2 Write the formula for the area of a parallelogram with base *b* and height *h*.

　　　Area =

Q3 Now write the same formula as a function using $f(x)$ for area and *x* for height. (Continue to use *b* for the constant base.)

To enter *b*, click on its measurement in the sketch. To enter *x*, click on the x in the dialog box.

12. Use the **Plot New Function** command from the Graph menu to plot your function from Q3.

Q4 How does the function plot relate to the path of the plotted point as you vary the height of the parallelogram?

Q5 Why does it make sense that the graph passes through the origin?

You can change the plot's domain by selecting it, choosing **Properties** from the Edit menu, and entering new values on the Plot panel.

Q6 The function is plotted beyond the sketch window in both directions. But actually, it should only include part of this. If you wanted the plot to accurately represent the situation, what part of it would you cut off? (In math terms, how would you restrict the *domain*?)

Direct Variation (continued)

Q7 In math jargon, we say that a parallelogram's area *varies directly with* (or *is directly proportional to*) its height when its base is held constant. Describe in your own words what you think this means.

13. Drag point *B* to change the length of the base of the parallelogram. Observe the effect this has on the graph.

Hint: One way to answer this is to compare a parallelogram that produces a steep graph to one that produces a gradual graph.

→ **Q8** How is the length of the base related to the slope of the (*height, area*) graph?

Explore More

1. Try dragging point *C* in such a way that the plotted point doesn't move (or barely moves) along the graph. Describe the path that *C* follows if you do this successfully. What does this illustrate about the area of a parallelogram?

Press down on the current **Arrow** tool icon and choose the **Dilate Arrow** tool from the palette that pops up.

→ 2. Mark point *A* as center, choose the **Dilate Arrow** tool, and drag point *D*. What happens to the graph? Describe the trace of the plotted point. Does the trace of the plotted point still coincide with the graph? Explain why or why not.

The Slope-Intercept Form of a Line   Name(s): _____

The slope-intercept form of a line, $y = mx + b$, is one of the best-known formulas in algebra. In this activity, you'll learn about this equation first by exploring one particular line, then by exploring whole *families* of lines.

Plotting One Particular Line

You'll start this activity with $m = 2$ and $b = 1$ as you explore the line $y = 2x + 1$. The focus will on the role of the *variables x* and *y*.

To hide the points, select them and choose **Hide Points** from the Display menu.

→ 1. In a new sketch, choose **Define Coordinate System** from the Graph menu. Hide the new points at (0, 0) and (1, 0).

Q1 For $y = 2x + 1$, what is y when $x = 0$? (Write your answer as an ordered pair.) Why does it make sense that we call this point the *y-intercept*?

Enter the coordinates in the Plot Points dialog box, click Plot, then click Done.

→ 2. Plot the point you found in Q1 using the **Plot Points** command in the Graph menu.

Q2 You found that the *y*-intercept of $y = 2x + 1$ is 1. Similarly, the *y*-intercept of $y = 3x + 7$ is 7. Explain why the *y*-intercept of $y = mx + b$ is always (0, b).

You've learned that *slope* can be thought of as *rise/run*. The slope of the line $y = 2x + 1$ is 2, which you can think of as 2/1 (*rise* = 2 and *run* = 1).

3. With the point (0, 1) selected, choose **Translate** from the Transform menu. Choose the Rectangular option. Type 1 for Horizontal (the "run") and 2 for Vertical (the "rise"). Click Translate.

   A second point is plotted, 1 unit to the right of the y-intercept and 2 units above it.

Q3 What are the coordinates of this new point? Plug them into the equation $y = 2x + 1$ to show that the point is indeed on the line.

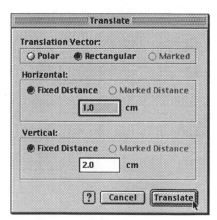

Step 3

4. Using the same technique, translate the newly plotted point by the same *rise* and *run* values to get a third point. Figure out the coordinates of this third point and verify that it satisfies the equation $y = 2x + 1$.

5. Select any two of the three points you've plotted and choose **Line** from the Construct menu.

What you've done so far can be thought of as a general technique for plotting lines in $y = mx + b$ form. Let's summarize:

- Start by plotting the y-intercept $(0, b)$.

If *m* is a decimal such as 1.5, write it as a fraction such as 3/2. If it's a whole number such as 3, write it as a fraction such as 3/1.

- Rewrite *m* as *rise/run* (if necessary).

- Find a second point on the graph by translating the y-intercept by the *rise* and *run* values.

- Connect the two points to get the line. (You may also want to plot a third point just to be sure.)

Q4 Using the method described above, plot the following lines on graph paper.

a. $y = 3x - 2$ b. $y = (2/3)x + 2$

c. $y = -2x + 1$ d. $y = 2.5x - 3$

Exploring Whole Families of Lines

Now that you know how to plot individual lines in slope-intercept form, we'll focus on how the two *parameters*—*m* and *b*—affect the equation.

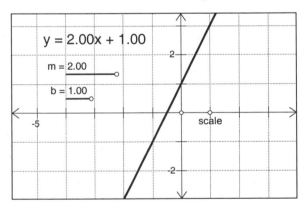

6. Open the sketch **Slope Intercept.gsp** from the folder **2_Lines**.

   You'll see a coordinate system with the equation $y = 2x + 1$ plotted. You can change the values of m and b by adjusting their sliders.

To adjust a slider, drag the point at its tip.

Q5 Adjust *m*'s slider and observe the effect this has on the line. How would you describe the difference between lines with positive *m* (slope), lines with negative *m,* and lines where $m = 0$?

Q6 Now adjust *b*'s slider and observe the effect this has on the line. What happens to the line as *b* becomes increasingly positive? Increasingly negative?

If at any point you wish to erase traces left by the line, choose **Erase Traces** from the Display menu.

→ 7. Select the line and choose **Trace Line** from the Display menu.

Q7 Adjust *m*'s slider and observe the trace pattern that forms. How would you describe the *family* of lines that forms when varying *m*?

Q8 Now adjust *b*'s slider. How would you describe the *family* of lines that forms when varying *b*?

Note: In this activity, the precision of measurements has been set to two decimal places. It's important to be aware of this and to check your answers by hand, in addition to adjusting the sliders in the sketch.

→ **Q9** Write the equation in slope-intercept form for each of the lines described. As a check, adjust the *m* and *b* sliders so that the line is drawn on the screen.

a. slope is 2.0 and the *y*-intercept is (0, –3)

b. slope is –1.5 and the *y*-intercept is (0, 4)

c. slope is 3.0 and the *x*-intercept is (–2, 0)

d. slope is –0.4 and contains the point (–6, 2)

e. contains the points (3, 5) and (–1, 3)

Explore More

1. Attempt to construct a line through the points (3, 0) and (3, –3) by adjusting the sliders in the sketch. Explain why this is impossible (implying that its equation cannot be written in slope-intercept form).

2. Is it possible to construct the same line with different slider configurations? If not, explain why. If so, provide two different equations for the same line.

Exploring Algebra with The Geometer's Sketchpad
© 2002 Key Curriculum Press

The Point-Slope Form of a Line   Name(s): _____

The slope-intercept form of a line is great if you know one special point: the *y*-intercept. But what if the point you know is an everyday, ordinary point such as (3, –2) or (–7, –7)? In this case, it's usually most convenient to use the *point-slope form* of a line, which you'll study in this activity.

Sketch and Investigate

1. Open the sketch **Point Slope.gsp**.

To adjust a slider, drag the point at its tip. → *You'll see an equation in the point-slope form y = m(x – h) + k, with m, h, and k filled in. Adjust the sliders for m, h, and k and watch the equation change. There's no line yet because we wanted you to get practice graphing in Sketchpad.*

2. Choose **Plot New Function** from the Graph menu.

   The New Function dialog box appears.

To enter m, h, and k, click on their measurements in the sketch. To enter x, click on x in the dialog box. → 3. Enter *m(x – h) + k* and click OK.

   Sketchpad plots the function for the current values of the parameters m, h, and k.

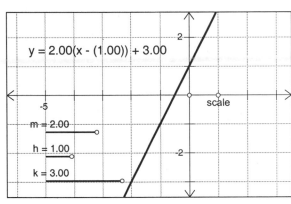

y = 2.00(x - (1.00)) + 3.00

m = 2.00

h = 1.00

k = 3.00

scale

*If at any point you wish to erase traces left by the line, choose **Erase Traces** from the Display menu.* → 4. With the new line selected, choose **Trace Function Plot** from the Display menu.

Q1 Adjust *m*'s slider. You'll see that the line rotates around a single point. Change the values of *h* and *k*, then adjust *m* again, focusing on where this point appears to be.

What are the point's coordinates in terms of *h* and *k*?

You may have noticed that the line rotates around the point (*h, k*). To verify this, you'll now plot that point.

5. Deselect all objects. Now select, in order, *h*'s measurement and *k*'s measurement. Choose **Plot As (x, y)** from the Graph menu to plot the selected measurements as an (*x, y*) pair.

   Adjust m's slider again. Was your conjecture from Q1 correct?

The Point-Slope Form of a Line (continued)

Q2 How would you describe the *family* of lines that forms when varying *m*?

Q3 Adjust *h* and *k*'s sliders. How would you describe the *families* of lines that form when varying *h* and *k*? How do they compare to each other?

Q4 Summarize the roles that *h* and *k* play in the equation $y = m(x - h) + k$.

The point-slope form is probably more convenient than the slope-intercept form here since the point you know isn't the *y*-intercept. → **Q5** Suppose you know that the slope of a particular line is 2 and that it contains the point (1, 3). What is the equation in point-slope form for this line?

Note: In this activity, the precision of measurements has been set to two decimal places. It's important to be aware of this and to check your answers by hand, in addition to adjusting the sliders in the sketch. → **Q6** Write an equation in point-slope form for each of the lines described. As a check, adjust the *m*, *h*, and *k* sliders so that the line is drawn on the screen.

    a. slope is 2; contains the point (–2, 1)

    b. slope is –1; contains the point (–2, 1)

    c. parallel to the line $y = 3(x - 2) + 4$; goes through the origin

    d. slope is 4/5; the *x*-intercept is (2, 0)

    e contains the points (2, 3) and (–1, 4)

    f. contains the points (–3, 5) and (4, 5)

Explore More

1. Attempt to construct the line through the points (2, 3) and (2, –2) by adjusting the sliders in the sketch. Explain why this is impossible (implying that its equation cannot be written in point-slope form).

2. Is it possible to construct the same line with different slider configurations? If not, explain why. If so, provide two different equations for the same line.

Exploring Algebra with The Geometer's Sketchpad
© 2002 Key Curriculum Press

The Standard Form of a Line

Name(s): _____

When in the form of Clark Kent, he's a scrappy reporter you'd ask to help expose government corruption; in the form of Superman, he's a superhero you'd ask to get your cat out of a tree or save the earth from obliteration. Same person, different forms. Similarly, the same line can take on different forms in terms of the equation used to describe it. And like Clark Kent/Superman, the different forms are useful in different ways.

In earlier activities, you explored the slope-intercept form $y = mx + b$ and the point-slope form $y = m(x - h) + k$. In this activity, you'll explore the standard form $Ax + By = C$. At first, this form may seem to convey less useful information than the other two. But as you'll soon see, understanding this form can lead to a whole new way of looking at lines.

Sketch and Investigate

1. Open the sketch **Standard.gsp**.

2. Adjust A's slider (by dragging the point at its tip) and observe the effect this has on the line—in particular, on the x-intercept.

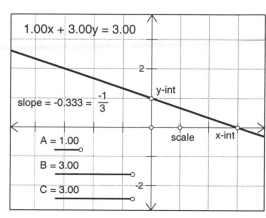

Select the two points and choose **Coordinates** *from the Measure menu.*

3. Measure the coordinates of the x- and y-intercepts.

Note: In this activity, the precision of measurements has been set to two decimal places. It's important to be aware of this and to check your answers by hand, in addition to adjusting the sliders in the sketch.

Q1 In the table below, fill in the x-intercept for the given values of A.

A:	2	3	6	12	−1	−3
x-intercept:						

4. Drag the point at slider A's tip slowly to the left, but keep A positive. Observe what happens to the x-intercept.

Q2 Write a conjecture on the relationship between the x-intercept and the values of A and C.

5. Make $C = 12.00$. Adjust B's slider and observe the effect this has on the line—in particular, on the y-intercept.

Q3 In the table below, fill in the y-intercept for the given values of B.

B:	2	3	6	12	−1	−3
y-intercept:						

6. Drag B slowly to the left, but keep its value positive. Notice what happens to the y-intercept.

Q4 Write a conjecture on the relationship between the y-intercept and the values of B and C.

7. Press the *Initial position* button to return the sketch to its original state. Now adjust C's slider, observing the line and the x- and y-intercepts.

8. Make $A = 2.00$ and $B = 4.00$. Now once again adjust C's slider and observe the behavior of the line and the axis intercepts.

Q5 Based on your observations thus far, write down formulas using A, B, and C for the quantities listed below. Check your formulas by algebraically manipulating the equation $Ax + By = C$.

x-intercept:

y-intercept:

slope:

A *vector* is a quantity with both a distance and a direction, such as 3 cm to the right. Vectors are often represented by arrows.

→ An important property of A and B is this: Vector $[A, B]$ is perpendicular to the line. To see this, press the *Show vector* button. The blue segment represents vector $[A, B]$. The *foot* of the vector has been arbitrarily placed at the y-intercept, and the *head* is represented by the arrowhead.

9. Adjust all three sliders and notice that the vector remains perpendicular to the line.

Q6 Find the equations of the following lines in standard form. First find the answers using paper and pencil, then check your answers by adjusting the sliders in the sketch.

   a. parallel to $3x - 4y = 12$; x-intercept at $(1, 0)$

   b. x-intercept at $(-5, 0)$; y-intercept at $(0, 2)$

   c. x-intercept at $(4, 0)$; containing the point $(2, 1)$

   d. perpendicular to the vector $[5, -3]$; passing through the origin

   e. perpendicular to the vector $[-2, 4]$; passing through $(5, 3)$

Solving Systems of Equations

Name(s): _____

Torrance and Claire love to race. But Torrance's leg is in a cast, so on this day Claire gives him a 1/2 km head start. (They start at the same time, but Torrance starts 1/2 km ahead of Claire.) Claire runs a kilometer in four minutes, but in his cast Torrance can only walk a kilometer in nine minutes. How long will it take Claire to catch up to Torrance?

One way to solve a problem like this is to model the situation with a graph of each racer's position over time. Since Torrance's motion can be modeled with one equation and Claire's with a second, you'll be using your graph to solve two equations at the same time. When you find numbers that satisfy two or more equations at once, you're solving a *system of equations*.

Sketch and Investigate

1. In a new sketch, choose **Define Coordinate System** from the Graph menu to create a set of coordinate axes.

> Click on an object with the **Text** tool to show its label. Double-click the label itself to change it.

2. Show the labels of the *x*- and *y*-axes. Then relabel the *x*-axis "*t*" (for time) and the *y*-axis "*d*" (for distance).

A good way to begin solving a word problem is to start with simple, concrete cases. The following questions and steps help you do that.

Q1 Pick an amount of time and determine how far Claire has run in that time period. Write this as an ordered pair (t, d). Let t represent time elapsed (in minutes) and d represent distance run (in kilometers).

Q2 Write a second ordered pair that represents another time and distance in Claire's run.

3. Use the **Plot Points** command from the Graph menu to plot the points corresponding to your two ordered pairs.

Q3 Which point in the sketch represents Claire's starting point?

Solving Systems of Equations (continued)

If Claire runs at a steady rate, you can model the distance she's run at any given time with a straight line. Why?

Choose the **Line** tool by pressing down on the current **Straightedge** tool and choosing the **Line** tool from the palette that pops up.

4. Use the **Line** tool to construct a line through the two plotted points. Label the line "Claire." Does the line pass through the starting point from Q3?

5. Use the same technique you used for Claire to construct a line modeling Torrance's distance from the starting line. (Don't forget to allow for his 1/2 km head start.) Label this line "Torrance."

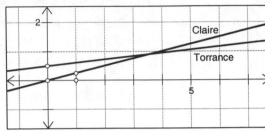

Q4 What physical feature of the graph corresponds with the moment when Claire catches up with Torrance?

Now you'll find the exact location of the point where Claire catches up with Torrance.

6. Select both lines and choose **Intersection** from the Construct menu to find the point of intersection.

With the point selected, choose **Coordinates** from the Measure menu.

7. Measure the coordinates of the point of intersection.

Q5 How much time has passed when Claire catches up with Torrance? How far have they each gone?

Select the lines and choose **Equations** from the Measure menu.

Q6 Measure the equations of both lines. Write the system of equations that models this problem.

Q7 Explain the meaning of *each* constant in each equation in your system. For example, what does the number 0.25 in Claire's equation have to do with the problem?

Exploring Algebra with The Geometer's Sketchpad
© 2002 Key Curriculum Press

Solving Systems of Equations (continued)

Q8 Using the **Line** tool, draw a third line anywhere in your sketch. Then measure its equation. Adjust the line to plausibly model a third person's distance from the starting line. (Perhaps this person is Rollerblading.) Describe your new racer below.

Name:

Speed:

Starting point:

When and where this racer meets Torrance:

When and where this racer meets Claire:

Equation that models this racer's trip:

Present Your Findings

Make a printout showing all the race participants. Describe the three competitors. Explain the equations that model their motion, and list the coordinates of all intersection points. You may also want to add a new line modeling a horse's or bicyclist's or anyone else's motion in the race.

Explore More

1. Not every system of two linear equations has a single solution. Try to make a sketch of a system of linear equations with more than one solution, then another one with no solutions. What's true of lines that fit these criteria? Now consider systems of three linear questions, or four, or even ten! How many solutions might they have?

2. Do a circle and a line always meet in exactly two points? Describe the possible solutions to a system where one equation models a circle and the other models a line. What if both equations model circles?

3. Our race model was a good one, but not entirely accurate. Explain why the model would have been more realistic if we had used the **Ray** tool instead of the **Line** tool. Can you think of other reasons why the model wasn't very accurate?

The Absolute Value Function
and the "V-Graph"

Name(s): _____

The absolute value of a number is how "big" the number is, regardless of whether it's positive or negative. Some examples should make this clearer.

The absolute value of –5 is 5,   or $|-5| = 5$.

The absolute value of 5 is 5,   or $|5| = 5$.

The absolute value of 0 is 0,   or $|0| = 0$.

As you can see, the absolute value of a number is always a positive number or 0.

But what happens when you graph an equation involving the absolute value function, such as $y = |2x - 4|$? In this activity, you'll find out.

Sketch and Investigate

Choose **Plot New Function** from the Graph menu. Type x and click OK.

→ 1. In a new sketch, plot the equation $y = x$.

2. Think about what the graph of $y = |x|$ might look like. Plotting points by hand or discussing the question with classmates might help. Make a rough sketch of your guess on scratch paper.

Choose **Plot New Function** from the Graph menu. Choose **abs** from the Functions pop-up menu, then enter x and click OK.

→ 3. Plot the equation $y = |x|$. How does it compare with your prediction?

4. Repeat steps 1 through 3 with the equations $y = 2x - 4$ and $y = |2x - 4|$. Make sure to draw a prediction of what you think the second equation will look like before plotting it in Sketchpad.

Q1 Describe how the graphs of $y = 2x - 4$ and $y = |2x - 4|$ compare. You might discuss their shapes and their ranges, among other things.

A Family of Absolute Value Graphs

As you explore this family, it may help to keep in mind a related family you may be familiar with: lines in point-slope form $y = m(x - h) + k$.

Now that you have an idea of what absolute values can do to the graphs of particular functions, you'll explore a *family* of graphs: $y = m|x - h| + k$.

5. Open the sketch **VGraph.gsp** from the folder **2_Lines**.

   You'll see the graph of an equation in the form $y = m|x - h| + k$, and sliders for the parameters m, h, and k.

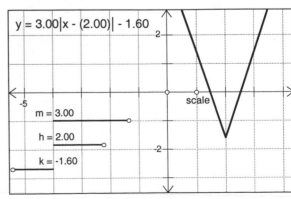

The "V-Graph" (continued)

V-graph is our term, not a standard mathematical term.

Q2 Adjust *m*'s slider and observe the effect this has on the "V-graph." Be sure to try out all different types of slopes—large, small, positive, negative, and zero.

In the space provided, summarize the role *m* plays in the equation $y = m|x - h| + k$.

Q3 You may have noticed that changing *m* changes all the points on the V-graph but one. This point is called the *vertex*. Adjust the sliders for *h* and *k* and then answer the following question.

How does the location of the vertex relate to the values of *h* and *k*?

Note: In this activity, the precision of measurements has been set to two decimal places. It's important to be aware of this and to check your answers by hand, in addition to adjusting the sliders in the sketch.

Q4 Write an equation in the form $y = m|x - h| + k$ for each of the V-graphs described below. As a check, adjust the *m*, *h*, and *k* sliders so that the V-graph described is drawn on the screen.

a. vertex at (–1, 2); contains the point (0, 4)

b. vertex at (2, 3); contains the point (4, 0)

c. vertex at (–3, –1); same shape as $y = 3|x - 2| + 5$

d. *x*-intercepts at (4, 0) and (–4, 0); contains the point (1, –2)

e. *x*-intercepts at (6, 0) and (–2, 0); contains the point (5, 1)

f. same vertex as $y = 3|x - 2| + 5$; contains the point (0, 0)

Explore More

To enter sin(x), choose **sin** from the Functions pop-up menu. If the Trigonometric Functions dialog box appears, click Yes.

1. Plot the following two pairs of equations: $y = x^2 - 1$ and $y = |x^2 - 1|$; $y = \sin(x)$ and $y = |\sin(x)|$. (Don't worry if you're unfamiliar with these functions.) Then write a short paragraph summarizing what happens when you plot a function and its absolute value.

Swans and Giraffes:
Introducing Linear Programming   Name(s): _____

In business, it's often difficult to figure out how to maximize profit because there are so many factors to consider: labor costs, time constraints, production capacity, etc. *Linear programming* is a branch of algebra that helps deal with complicated situations such as this.

Here's a typical linear programming problem:

Origami is the ancient Japanese art of paper folding.

> Rei volunteers to bring origami swans and giraffes to sell at a charity crafts fair. It takes her three minutes to make a swan and six minutes to make a giraffe. She plans to sell the swans for $4 each and the giraffes for $6 each. If she has only 16 pieces of origami paper and can't spend more than one hour folding, how many of each animal should Rei make to maximize the charity's profit?

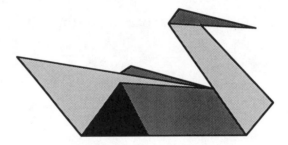

Assigning Variables and Writing the Profit Equation

As you can see, there's a lot of information to deal with here. Let's start by assigning variables. Since the actual question is "How many of each type of animal should Rei make?" we'll assign variables as follows:

> let x = the number of swans Rei makes

> let y = the number of giraffes Rei makes

Q1 Write an equation for profit in terms of x and y. (In other words, if Rei makes x swans and y giraffes, how much money will that bring in?)

Profit =

1. Open the sketch **Origami.gsp** from the folder **2_Lines**.

    You'll see a grid, a point R, R's x- and y-coordinate measurements, and the profit equation. Each location of point R is a potential solution to the problem. For example, (6, 8) represents a solution of six swans and eight giraffes. (Does the profit equation agree with the one you came up with?)

Exploring Algebra with The Geometer's Sketchpad
© 2002 Key Curriculum Press

Q2 Drag point R around and observe how the coordinate and profit measurements change. Describe how the profit relates to R's location in the plane. Where is profit greatest? Where is it smallest?

Choose **Snap Points** from the Graph menu if you wish to toggle point snapping off.

Q3 Sketchpad is set up with "point snapping" turned on, meaning that R will land only on locations with integer coordinates. Why does it make sense for point snapping to be turned on in this problem? Also, why does it make sense to consider only those locations of point R in the first quadrant (and on the positive x- and y-axes)?

Setting Up the Constraint Inequalities

The limitations discussed in Q3 are *implicit constraints:* constraints implied in the problem but not explicitly mentioned.

Obviously, the more origami figures made, the greater the profit. But this ignores the *constraints* (limitations) listed in the problem. The first constraint is that "she has only 16 pieces of origami paper." We'll refer to this as the *paper constraint* and express it mathematically with the *constraint inequality* $x + y \le 16$.

2. Go to page 2 of **Origami.gsp**.

   You'll see a new line and a new calculation. The line, $x + y = 16$, is the equation form of the paper constraint. The calculation, $x_R + y_R$, shows how many pieces of paper are used for the current point R.

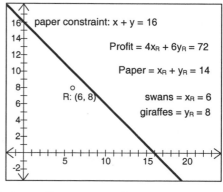

paper constraint: x + y = 16

Profit = 4x_R + 6y_R = 72

Paper = x_R + y_R = 14

R: (6, 8)

swans = x_R = 6

giraffes = y_R = 8

Q4 Where in the sketch can you drag R and have the paper constraint satisfied? Within that region, where is the profit greatest?

In the next two steps, you'll develop a similar inequality for the *time constraint*.

Q5 The problem states: "It takes her three minutes to make a swan and six minutes to make a giraffe." Use this information to write two expressions: one for how long it takes Rei to make *x* swans, and the other for how long it takes her to make *y* giraffes.

Q6 Use your expressions from Q5 to write a constraint inequality for the time constraint—that Rei "can't spend more than one hour folding."

3. Go to page 3 of **Origami.gsp**.

   A few more things have been added, including a blue line for the equation form of the time constraint. This line and the red line divide the first quadrant into four regions, each given a different color.

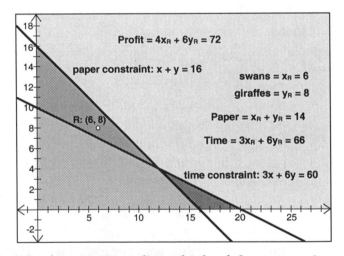

Q7 For each of the four regions, list which of the two major constraints (paper and time) are met and which aren't. In which region can you drag *R* and have both major constraints met?

Finding the Maximum

The region you found in Q5 in which both constraints are satisfied is called the *feasible region.* Your goal now is to find the one point within this region that maximizes profit. You can drag point R around and try to find where the highest profit occurs, but there's an easier way. Linear programmers can prove that *the maximum value always occurs at a corner point of the feasible region.* But which corner is it?

Simply click on the feasible region—the yellow quadrilateral— to select it.

→ 4. Select point R and the feasible region. Then choose **Merge Point To Quadrilateral** from the Edit menu. Point R will attach itself to the perimeter of the feasible region.

Q8 Drag point R around the perimeter of the feasible region, noting in particular the profit value at the corner points. How many swans and giraffes should Rei make in order to maximize profit? What is the maximum profit?

Explore More

1. Suppose that Rei actually has 18 pieces of paper. Modify the sketch as follows: Press the *Show Parameters* button on page 3, then double-click max_{paper} and change 16 to 18. How does this change the feasible region? Can Rei increase profits with this new feasible region?

2. Continue experimenting with changing the paper constraint. How much does the maximum profit increase with each extra figure?

3. Rei was limited by only two major constraints. What if a third were added? For instance, what if Rei didn't want to make more than eight giraffes? Turn this new constraint into a constraint inequality and describe the new feasible region as well as the maximum profit.

4. Go to page 4 of **Origami.gsp**. You'll see a new line labeled *profit.* Alternate between dragging point R along this new line and dragging the line itself. (Drag the line by dragging its y-intercept.) Explain what the new line represents. Then explain how it demonstrates why profit will always be maximized at a corner point of the feasible region.

An Ant's Progress: Modeling Linear Motion in Time

Name(s): _____

You notice an ant walking slowly across a piece of graph paper on your desk. You start your stopwatch the moment the ant is at point (–4, –5); one minute later, it has reached point (–1, –3). You find yourself wondering when the ant, if it keeps up this pace, will cross the y-axis and, after that, the x-axis.

Spend several minutes pondering this situation. For now, focus on understanding and picturing the situation rather than finding exact solutions. If you do come up with possible answers, write them down.

Investigate

Now that you have an understanding of the situation, let's look at several ways algebra and Sketchpad can help you explore the ant's walk.

Consider the following two equations, which together give the ant's location at any time t:

Equations like these are called *parametric equations*, and the letter t is called a *parameter*.

$$x = -4 + 3t \quad \text{and}$$
$$y = -5 + 2t, \quad \text{where } t \text{ is the number of minutes the ant has walked}$$

Q1 Use the equations above and the given values of t to fill in the table. To do this, plug the t-values into the equations to find the ant's (x, y) locations at the given times.

For example, for $t = 0$:
$$x = -4 + 3(0) = -4$$
$$y = -5 + 2(0) = -5$$

which confirms that the ant is at point (–4, –5) at time $t = 0$.

t:	0	1	2	3	4
x:	–4				
y:	–5				

Looking at the table and the grid may help you revise your estimate of when the ant will cross the y- and x-axes.

Q2 Plot each (x, y) pair from Q1 on the coordinate grid at right to show where the ant is after 0, 1, 2, 3, and 4 minutes.

Q3 What would the two parametric equations have been if the ant had started at point $(-2, 0)$ and reached point $(0, 1)$ after one minute?

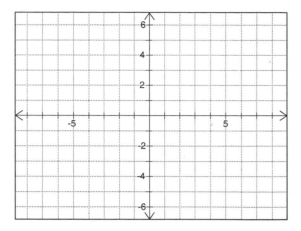

Sketch

1. Open the sketch **Ants Progress.gsp** in the folder **2_Lines**.

   You'll see a coordinate grid with a red line representing time; buttons for t = 0, 1, 2, 3, and 4; the parametric equations; and, of course, an ant.

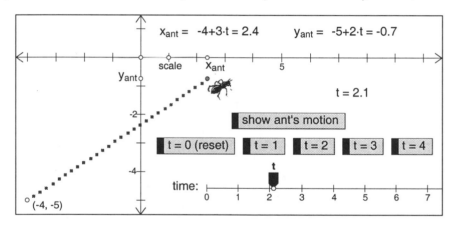

2. Try the following to get familiar with the sketch:

   • Move the ant along its path by dragging point t.

   • Press the buttons for $t = 0, 1, 2, 3,$ and 4. Compare the ant's locations in the sketch with the positions you plotted by hand.

Hint: Recall that all points on the y-axis have an x-coordinate of zero, and all points on the x-axis have a y-coordinate of zero.

Q4 Use the parametric equations themselves to determine the exact times when the ant crosses the x- and y-axes. Use the sketch to check your answers, then write them below.

To construct the line, select the two points and choose **Line** from the Construct menu. With the line selected, choose **Equation** from the Measure menu.

Q5 Construct a line through the ant's point and the point at (–4, –5). Select the line and measure its equation. How does this equation relate to the two parametric equations?

To edit the parametric equations, double-click them. To enter t into the dialog box that appears, click on its measurement in the sketch.

Q6 Consider the following motion: The ant starts at (5, 1) and heads toward (–7, 19). Edit the sketch to model this situation, then test the model by pressing the action buttons. Write your equations below.

Q7 How would the equations in Q6 change if we insisted that the ant travel the same speed as at the beginning of the activity? Edit the sketch to model this situation, test the model by pressing the action buttons, then write your equations below.

Chapter 2: Slope and Lines
Project Ideas

The projects below extend your knowledge of slope and lines and are suitable for in-class presentations, papers, or personal exploration.

1. In the Explore More question from the activity The Slope of a Line, you were asked to think of other kinds of descriptions (besides slope) that might be used to describe the steepness of things. One possible answer to this is *angle*. Specifically, one can describe the steepness of a line in the *x-y* plane by the acute angle it makes with the *x*-axis. What is the mathematical relationship between this angle and the slope measurement you studied in this chapter? Create a Sketchpad sketch demonstrating this relationship. (*Hint:* If you've studied the tangent function, that will be useful here.)

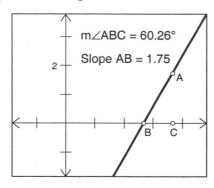

m∠ABC = 60.26°

Slope AB = 1.75

2. In the activity How Slope Is Measured, you learned that slope is defined as *rise/run*. What would be the consequences if slope were defined instead as *run/rise*? Why do you think mathematicians chose *rise/run*? Support your argument by making a sketch that shows the slope of a line if slope were defined the other way.

3. In the activity Solving Systems of Equations, the names Torrance and Claire were chosen to honor the famous racing rivals the Tortoise and the Hare. Long before the Hare joined the race, however, the Tortoise was racing Achilles in ancient Greek philosopher Zeno's famous paradox. Look up "Zeno's Paradox" at the library or on the web and present a report on your findings. Can you create a Sketchpad sketch, perhaps using Move buttons, that models the race described in the paradox?

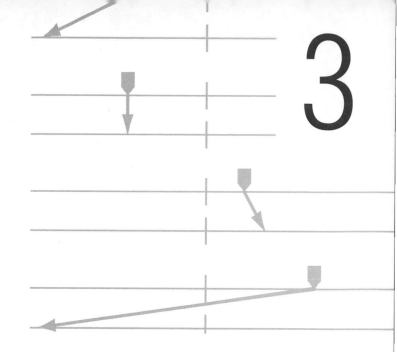

Parabolas and
Quadratic Equations

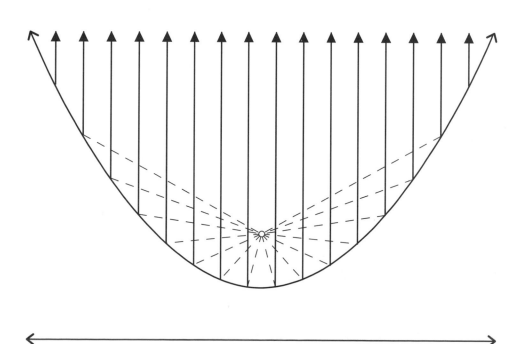

Where Are the Giant Ants?

Name(s): _____

Many monster movies have featured gigantic ants or other insects attacking and destroying cities. Did you ever wonder why such giant bugs don't exist outside the movies? Or why there aren't miniature elephants or elephant-sized insects? The answer to these questions actually relates to the evolution of species, including humans! Before tackling animals and humans, we'll scale down from three dimensions to two as you look at some "flat animals"—namely, polygons.

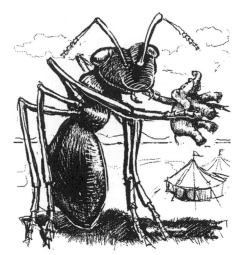

Sketch and Investigate

In this activity, you'll explore what happens to a polygon's measurements as it gets bigger and smaller. So first, you'll need to construct a polygon and its interior.

1. In a new sketch, use the **Segment** tool to draw a polygon of four to six sides.

   Each segment (after the first) should share an endpoint with the previous one. The last segment should connect back to the first. When you're done, you should have the same number of points as segments.

2. With the **Arrow** tool, click in blank space to deselect all objects. Now select all of the points consecutively around the polygon and choose **Interior** from the Construct menu.

   You should now have a polygon and its interior.

Next you'll make a scale copy of your interior. You'll use the ratio of the lengths of two segments as the scale factor, which will allow you to change the scale factor just by dragging.

Click on an object with the **Text** tool to show its label. Double-click the label itself to change it.

3. Using the **Segment** tool, construct segments AB and CD.

4. Select, in order, $\overline{AB}$ and $\overline{CD}$; then choose **Ratio** from the Measure menu.

5. With the new ratio measurement still selected, choose **Mark Scale Factor** from the Transform menu.

   A brief animation indicates that the measurement has been marked as a scale factor.

$$\frac{m\,\overline{AB}}{m\,\overline{CD}} = 1.37$$

6. Using the **Point** tool, draw a point outside the polygon. With the point still selected, choose **Mark Center** from the Transform menu.

A brief animation indicates that the point has been marked as a center.

Dilation is a transformation that scales an object away from or toward a point.

7. To construct the scale copy, select the sides, vertices, and interior of the polygon and choose **Dilate** from the Transform menu. Click OK to dilate by the marked ratio.

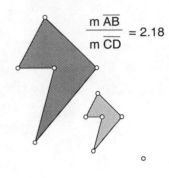

$$\frac{m \overline{AB}}{m \overline{CD}} = 2.18$$

The scale image appears. Drag point B to experiment with changing the scale factor. What happens when $\overline{AB}$ is bigger than $\overline{CD}$? Equal? Smaller? What if $\overline{AB} = 0$? Also experiment with dragging the center point and the vertices of your polygon.

8. Select a side of the scaled polygon, then a *corresponding* side of the original polygon. Measure the ratio of these two segments.

9. Measure the perimeters of the two polygon interiors by selecting them and choosing **Perimeter** from the Measure menu.

Choose **Calculate** from the Measure menu to open Sketchpad's Calculator. Click on the perimeter measurements in the sketch to enter them into the calculation.

10. Calculate the ratio of the perimeter of the scaled interior to the perimeter of the original interior.

Q1 How do the ratios of side lengths and perimeters compare with the scale factor you used for dilation?

Comparing Areas

You can think of perimeter as the "flat elephant's" waist, and area as its skin. When the elephant's waist grows twice as big, what happens to the area of its skin? Think about this a moment before moving on.

Repeat steps 9 and 10, choosing **Area** instead of **Perimeter**.

11. Measure the areas of the two polygon interiors, then calculate the ratio of these two measurements.

Did you get the ratio you predicted? Drag point B until you've confirmed or refuted your prediction.

Q2 What have you discovered about the relationship between the ratio of lengths of similar figures and the ratio of areas of these figures?

Exploring Algebra with The Geometer's Sketchpad
© 2002 Key Curriculum Press

Where Are the Giant Ants? (continued)

Often, mathematical relationships become clearer when they are graphed. Next, you'll plot the ratio of side lengths versus the ratio of areas for different scale factors.

12. Select, in order, the side-length ratio calculation and the area ratio calculation. Choose **Plot As (x, y)** from the Graph menu.

    A coordinate system appears along with the plotted point. The coordinates of this point are (side-length ratio, area ratio) for the current scale factor.

Choose **Erase Traces** from the Display menu if you wish to clear traces from the screen.

→13. With the newly plotted point still selected, choose **Trace Plotted Point** from the Display menu. Drag point *B* to experiment with different scale factors. Also drag the vertices of your polygon around—does anything change?

Q3 Explain why the shape of the graph makes sense given the relationship you discovered in Q2.

Explore More

1. Your polygon probably didn't look much like a flat elephant. For one thing, it was a little pointy. Determine whether or not the relationship you found in this activity would hold for "curvier" shapes like the ones at right. (*Hint:* Try using a circle instead of a polygon for the above investigation.)

2. Let's move back to three dimensions. How does the ratio of the volumes of similar solids compare to the ratio of corresponding side lengths? Predict the answer, then investigate by calculating the volumes of two boxes, one twice as long, tall, and wide as the other.

3. What do you think the graph of side-length ratio versus perimeter ratio would look like? Make a prediction, then test it in Sketchpad.

4. The introduction to this activity discussed the sizes of animals. How do you think the results (including the previous Explore More question) help to explain why ants the size of elephants can't exist. (*Hint:* Animals' volumes are proportional to their masses.)

Parabolas in Vertex Form

Name(s): _____

Things with *bilateral symmetry*—such as the human body—have parts on the sides that come in pairs (such as ears and feet) and parts down the middle there's just one of (such as the nose and bellybutton). Parabolas are the same way. Points on one side have corresponding points on the other. But one point is unique: the vertex. It's right in the middle, and—like your nose—there's just one of it. Not surprisingly, there's a common equation form for parabolas that relates to this unique point.

Sketch and Investigate

1. Open the sketch **Vertex Form.gsp** from the folder **3_Quads**.

   You'll see an equation in the form $y = a(x – h)^2 + k$, with a, h, and k filled in, and sliders for a, h, and k. Adjust the sliders (by dragging the points at their tips) and watch the equation change accordingly. There's no graph yet because we wanted you to practice using Sketchpad's graphing features.

2. Choose **Plot New Function** from the Graph menu.

   The New Function dialog box appears. If necessary, move it so that you can see a, h, and k's measurements.

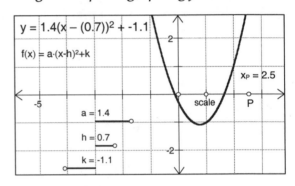

To enter *a*, *h*, and *k*, click on their measurements in the sketch. To enter *x*, click on the *x* in the dialog box.

3. Enter `a*(x–h)^2+k` and click OK.

   Sketchpad plots the function for the current values of a, h, and k.

   You'll now plot the point on the parabola whose *x*-coordinate is the same as point *P*'s.

Choose **Calculate** from the Measure menu. Click on the function equation from step 3. Then click on x_P to enter it. Now type a close parenthesis—")"— and click OK.

4. Calculate $f(x_P)$, the value of the function *f* evaluated at x_P.

   You'll see an equation for $f(x_P)$, the value of the function f evaluated at x_P.

5. Select, in order, x_P and $f(x_P)$; then choose **Plot As (x, y)** from the Graph menu.

   A point is plotted on the parabola.

Q1 Using paper and pencil or a calculator, show that the coordinates of the new point satisfy the parabola's equation. Write your calculation below. If the numbers are a little off, explain why this might be.

Exploring Algebra with The Geometer's Sketchpad
© 2002 Key Curriculum Press

Exploring Families of Parabolas

By dragging point P, you're exploring how the variables x and y vary along *one particular parabola* with particular values for a, h, and k. For the rest of this activity, you'll change the values of a, h, and k, which will *change the parabola itself,* allowing you to explore whole families of parabolas.

Q2 Adjust a's slider and observe the effect on the parabola. Summarize a's role in the equation $y = a(x - h)^2 + k$. Be sure to discuss a's sign (whether it's positive or negative), its magnitude (how big or small it is), and anything else that seems important.

Q3 Dragging a appears to change all the points on the parabola but one: the *vertex*. Change the values of h and k; then adjust a again, focusing on where the vertex appears to be.

How does the location of the vertex relate to the values of h and k?

Q4 Adjust the sliders for h and k. Describe how the parabola transforms as h's value changes. How does that compare to the transformation that occurs as k's value changes?

Here's how the **Plot As (x, y)** command in the Graph menu works: Select two measurements and choose the command. Sketchpad plots a point whose x-coordinate is the first selected measurement and whose y-coordinate is the second selected measurement.

6. Use **Plot As (x, y)** to plot the vertex of your parabola.

Parabolas in Vertex Form (continued)

Note: In this activity, the precision of measurements has been set to two decimal places. It's important to be aware of this and to check your answers by hand, in addition to adjusting the sliders in the sketch.

Q5 Write the equation in vertex form $y = a(x - h)^2 + k$ for each parabola described. As a check, adjust the sliders so that the parabola is drawn on the screen.

    a. vertex at $(1, -1)$; y-intercept at $(0, 4)$

    b. vertex at $(-4, -3)$; contains the point $(-2, -1)$

    c. vertex at $(5, 2)$; contains the point $(1, -6)$

    d. same vertex as the parabola $-3(x - 2)^2 - 2$; contains the point $(0, 6)$

    e. same shape as the parabola $4(x + 3)^2 - 1$; vertex at $(-1, 3)$

Q6 The *axis of symmetry* is the line over which a parabola can be flipped and still look the same. What is the equation of the axis of symmetry for the parabola $y = 2(x - 3)^2 + 1$? for $y = a(x - h)^2 + k$?

Q7 Just as your right ear has a corresponding ear across your body's axis of symmetry, all points on a parabola (except the vertex) have corresponding points across its axis of symmetry.

The point $(5, 9)$ is on the parabola $y = 2(x - 3)^2 + 1$. What is the corresponding point across the axis of symmetry?

Explore More

1. Assume that the point (s, t) is on the right half of the parabola $y = a(x - h)^2 + k$. What is the corresponding point across the axis of symmetry? If (s, t) were on the left half of the parabola, what would the answer be?

2. Use the **Perpendicular Line** command from the Construct menu to construct the axis of symmetry of your parabola. Then use the **Reflect** command from the Transform menu to reflect point P across the new axis of symmetry. Measure the coordinates of the new point, P'. Are they what you expected?

Exploring Algebra with The Geometer's Sketchpad
© 2002 Key Curriculum Press

Exploring Parabolas in Vertex Form

Name(s): _____

This activity is designed as an open-ended alternative to its step-by-step cousin, Parabolas in Vertex Form (page 76). Play with the various pages in the sketchbook **Explore Vertex.gsp** and let your curiosity be your guide. The questions below are meant to point you toward interesting areas of inquiry, but you or your teacher may decide that other questions are more interesting or relevant. Happy exploring!

The Sketchbook

Open the multi-page sketch **Explore Vertex.gsp** from the folder **3_Quads**. Use the link buttons to navigate from page to page. The various pages are described below.

$y = x^2$: **The Basic Parabola**	The vanilla parabola, the base model: no frills, no coefficients, nothing added or subtracted. Understand this parabola and you're well on your way to understanding them all.
$y = ax^2$ **(slider control)** $y = ax^2$ **(direct control)**	What happens when you multiply x^2 by a constant? Find out on these two pages. On the first, the parameter a is controlled by a slider. On the second, it's controlled directly by a point on the parabola. The underlying math is the same for both.
$y = ax^2 + k$ **(slider control)** $y = ax^2 + k$ **(direct control)**	What happens when you add a constant k to ax^2? Again, a and k are controlled with sliders on one page and directly with points on the parabola on the other, but the math is the same.
$y = a(x - h)^2 + k$ **(slider control)** $y = a(x - h)^2 + k$ **(direct control)**	What happens when you now subtract a constant h from the x in $y = ax^2 + k$? Find out here.

Questions to ponder, discuss, or write about

Q1 Name all of the points on $y = x^2$ that are visible in the current window and that have integers for both x- and y-coordinates. Without scrolling, name four other points on $y = x^2$ with integer coordinates.

Q2 What can you say about the equation of a parabola if its vertex is at the origin?

Q3 What kind of symmetry do all parabolas in the family $y = ax^2$ exhibit? Why do they have this symmetry?

Q4 If the point (a, b) is on the parabola $y = x^2$, name one other point that must be on the parabola.

Q5 How does the sign of a affect the parabolas on these pages?

Q6 What do the various graphs look like if $a = 0$?

Q7 How is the coefficient a in these equations similar to the coefficient m in $y = mx$, $y = mx + b$, and $y = m(x - h) + k$? How is it different?

Q8 On the fourth page—$y = ax^2$ (direct control)—a is controlled by a drag control located one unit to the right of the axis of symmetry (the y-axis). Why does it make sense for the drag control to be there?

Q9 The *axis of symmetry* is the line a parabola can be flipped over and still look the same. The axis of symmetry for $y = x^2$ is $x = 0$ (the y-axis). What is the equation of the axis of symmetry for parabolas in the family $y = ax^2$? $y = ax^2 + k$? $y = a(x - h)^2 + k$?

Q10 The four fundamental transformations in geometry are translation, rotation, dilation, and reflection. Look up these four terms, then describe which apply to the transformations to parabolas you observe when dragging the sliders for a, h, and k.

Explore More

1. Use commands from the Graph and/or Construct menus to construct the axis of symmetry of the parabola on one of the last two pages. Then use commands from the Transform menu to reflect point P across this axis.

Parabolas in Factored Form

Name(s): _____

When using a parabola to model the path of a baseball, you might want to know exactly where the ball hits the ground. Or when modeling a profit function with a quadratic, you might be interested in the *break even point*—the cutoff between profitability and loss. In both cases, you're interested in the *roots* of the equation—where it equals 0. In this activity, you'll explore a quadratic form that's useful in situations such as these.

Sketch and Investigate

1. Open the sketch **Factored Form.gsp** from the folder **3_Quads**.

   You'll see an equation in the form $y = a(x - p)(x - q)$ with a, p, and q filled in, and sliders for a, p, and q. Adjust the sliders (by dragging the points at their tips) and watch the equation change accordingly. There's no graph yet because we wanted you to practice using Sketchpad's graphing features.

2. Choose **Plot New Function** from the Graph menu.

   The New Function dialog box appears. If necessary, move it so that you can see a, p, and q's measurements.

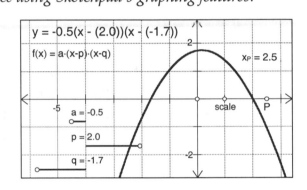

To enter *a*, *p*, and *q*, click on their measurements in the sketch. To enter *x*, click on the x in the dialog box. →

3. Enter a*(x–p)*(x–q) and click OK.

   Sketchpad plots the function you entered for the current values of the parameters a, p, and q.

You'll now plot the point on the parabola whose *x*-coordinate is the same as point *P*'s.

Choose **Calculate** from the Measure menu. Click on the function equation from step 3. Then click on x_P to enter it. Now type a close parenthesis—")"— and click OK. →

4. Calculate $f(x_P)$, the value of the function *f* evaluated at x_P.

   You'll see an equation for $f(x_P)$, the value of the function f evaluated at x_P.

5. Select, in order, x_P and $f(x_P)$; then choose **Plot As (x, y)** from the Graph menu.

   A point is plotted on the parabola.

Q1 Using paper and pencil or a calculator, show that the coordinates of the new point satisfy the parabola's equation. Write your calculation below. If the numbers are a little off, explain why this might be.

Exploring Families of Parabolas

By dragging point P, you're exploring how the variables x and y vary along *one particular parabola* with particular values for a, p, and q. For the rest of this activity, you'll change the values of a, p, and q, which *changes the parabola itself,* allowing you to explore whole families of parabolas.

Q2 Adjust a's slider and observe the effect on the parabola.

Summarize a's role in the equation $y = a(x - p)(x - q)$. Be sure to discuss a's sign (whether it's positive or negative), its magnitude (how big or small it is), and anything else that seems important.

Q3 Dragging a appears to change all the points on the parabola but two: the *x-intercepts* of the parabola, or the *roots*. Adjust all three sliders and observe the effects they each have on the x-intercepts.

How does the location of the x-intercepts relate to the values of the three sliders?

Q4 Adjust p's slider. What happens to the parabola as p's value changes? How does this compare to adjusting q's slider?

Q5 Adjust the sliders so that $p = q$. How would you describe the graph of a parabola with two equal roots?

Parabolas in Factored Form (continued)

Note: In this activity, the precision of measurements has been set to two decimal places. It's important to be aware of this and to check your answers by hand, in addition to adjusting the sliders in the sketch.

Q6 Write the equation in factored form $y = a(x - p)(x - q)$ for each parabola described. As a check, adjust the sliders so that the parabola is drawn on the screen.

  a. x-intercepts at $(-4, 0)$ and $(6, 0)$; vertex at $(1, -1)$

  b. x-intercepts at $(-5, 0)$ and $(1, 0)$; contains the point $(3, 32)$

  c. x-intercepts at $(0, 0)$ and $(-3, 0)$; contains the point $(2, 3)$

  d. same x-intercepts as $y = 2(x - 3)(x + 1)$; contains the point $(0, -3)$

  e. same shape as $y = 2(x - 3)(x + 1)$; x-intercepts at $(-4, 0)$ and $(1, 0)$

Q7 You throw a baseball and it flies in a parabolic path across a field. If the ball reaches its apex (highest point) of 20 feet above a point 60 feet away from you, how far away from you will the ball land? What is the equation of the ball's flight in factored form? Assume that the ball starts at the point $(0, 0)$.

Explore More

1. When you have a parabola in the form $y = a(x - h)^2 + k$, it's easy to find its vertex, but harder to find its roots. The opposite is true with the form $y = a(x - p)(x - q)$. Explain what you *do* know about the vertex of parabolas in this form. Can you write an expression for the x-coordinate of the vertex in terms of p and q? The y-coordinate?

2. In the sketch, construct or plot the parabola's vertex. If you do this properly, the point should remain the vertex regardless of how you drag the sliders. One way to do this would be to use Sketchpad's Calculator to calculate the x- and y-coordinates of the vertex using the expressions you found in the previous Explore More. You'd then select the two calculations and use the **Plot As (x, y)** command.

3. If you've done the previous Explore More, try this: Put a trace on the vertex by selecting it and choosing **Trace Plotted Point** from the Display menu. Now adjust p's slider. What shape does the vertex trace? Can you write an equation for this curve in terms of a and q?

Parabolas in Standard Form

Name(s): _____

You've seen that the vertex form of a parabola, $y = a(x - h)^2 + k$, and the factored form, $y = a(x - p)(x - q)$, both provide useful information about the graphs they describe. Perhaps the most common equation form for parabolas, though, is the standard form, $y = ax^2 + bx + c$. Equations in this form also provide useful information about their graphs, but as you'll soon see, this information takes a little more effort to discover.

Sketch and Investigate

1. Open the sketch **Standard Form.gsp**.

   You'll see an equation in the form $y = ax^2 + bx + c$ with a, b, and c filled in, and sliders for a, b, and c. Adjust the sliders (by dragging the points at their tips) and watch the equation change accordingly. There's no graph yet because we wanted you to practice using Sketchpad's graphing features.

2. Choose **Plot New Function** from the Graph menu.

   The New Function dialog box appears. If necessary, move it until you can see a, b, and c's measurements.

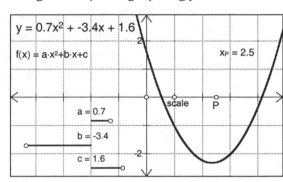

To enter a, b, and c, click on their measurements in the sketch. To enter x, click on the x in the dialog box. →

3. Enter `a*x^2+b*x+c` and click OK.

   Sketchpad plots the function you entered for the current values of the parameters a, b, and c.

   You'll now plot the point on the parabola whose x-coordinate is the same as point *P*'s.

Choose **Calculate** from the Measure menu. Click on the function equation from step 3. Then click on x_P to enter it. Now type a close parenthesis—")"— and click OK. →

4. Calculate $f(x_P)$, the value of the function f evaluated at x_P.

   You'll see an equation for $f(x_P)$, the value of the function f evaluated at x_P.

5. Select, in order, x_P and $f(x_P)$; then choose **Plot As (x, y)** from the Graph menu.

   A point is plotted on the parabola.

Q1 Using paper and pencil or a calculator, show that the coordinates of the new point satisfy the parabola's equation. Write your calculation below. If the numbers are a little off, explain why this might be.

Parabolas in Standard Form (continued)

Exploring Families of Parabolas

By dragging point P, you're exploring how the variables x and y vary along *one particular parabola* with particular values for a, b, and c. For the rest of this activity, you'll change the values of a, b, and c, which *changes the parabola itself*, allowing you to explore whole families of parabolas.

Q2 Adjust a's slider and observe the effect on the parabola.

Summarize a's role in the equation $y = ax^2 + bx + c$. Be sure to discuss a's sign (whether it's positive or negative), its magnitude (how big or small it is), and anything else that seems important.

Q3 Dragging a appears to change all the points on the parabola but one: the y-intercept. Adjust all three sliders and observe the effects they each have on the y-intercept.

How does the location of the y-intercept relate to the values of the three sliders?

Q4 Adjust c's slider. Describe how the parabola transforms as c's value changes.

Q5 Adjust b's slider. What happens to the parabola as b's value changes?

Parabolas in Standard Form (continued)

The *axis of symmetry* is the line a parabola can be flipped over and still look the same. In the next several steps, you'll show that the axis of symmetry for any parabola in standard form is the vertical line $x = -b/(2a)$.

To enter *a* and *b*, click on their measurements in the sketch.

6. Choose **Plot New Function** from the Graph menu. Then choose **x = f(y)** from the Equation pop-up menu in the dialog box that appears. Now enter $-b/(2*a)$ and click OK.

7. Make the new line dashed by selecting it and choosing **Dashed** from the Display | Line Weight submenu.

Q6 Write the equations in standard form for three parabolas with different *a* values that have the same axis of symmetry. Check your work by adjusting the sliders in the sketch.

Note: In this activity, the precision of measurements has been set to two decimal places. It's important to be aware of this and to check your answers by hand, in addition to adjusting the sliders in the sketch.

Q7 Write the equation in standard form $ax^2 + bx + c$ for each of the parabolas described. You may wish to start with a more convenient form, then convert to standard form. As a check, adjust the sliders so that the parabola is drawn on the screen.

a. vertex at $(2, 2)$; *y*-intercept at $(0, 4)$

b. vertex at $(-2, 3)$; contains the point $(0, 11)$

c. *x*-intercepts at $(-3, 0)$ and $(5, 0)$; vertex at $(1, -4)$

d. contains the points $(0, -4)$, $(1, -1)$, and $(2, 1)$

Explore More

1. The *quadratic formula*, which gives the roots of a parabola in terms of a, b, and c, is usually written $x_{roots} = \dfrac{-b \pm \sqrt{b^2 - 4ac}}{2a}$. By the rules of fraction addition, the right side can also be written as $\dfrac{-b}{2a} \pm \dfrac{\sqrt{b^2 - 4ac}}{2a}$. You've already seen that the first part of this expression represents the *x*-value of the axis of symmetry. Show that the second part of the expression represents the distance from the axis of symmetry to each of the roots. *(Very challenging!)*

Parabolas: A Geometric Approach   Name(s): _____

You may think of algebra and geometry as two very different branches of mathematics. In many ways they are. But you've seen that algebraic equations, such as $y = x + 3$, can be graphed as lines. And lines are certainly geometric objects. Now you're studying parabolas—the graphs of equations such as $y = x^2 + 3$. Can parabolas be described geometrically, without using algebraic equations? In this activity you'll see that they can.

Introduction

A *circle* can be described as the set of points in a plane that are the same distance from a fixed point—the center. Similarly, a *parabola* can be described as follows:

> A *parabola* is the set of points in a plane that are the same distance from a fixed point—the *focus*—as from a fixed line—the *directrix*.

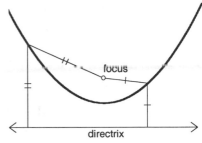

This is a more complicated definition than the circle's, but as you do this activity it should make more and more sense.

Sketch and Investigate

If the **Line** tool isn't showing, press down on the current **Straightedge** tool and choose the **Line** tool from the palette that pops up.

1. In a new sketch, choose **Preferences** from the Edit menu. On the Text panel, check For All New Points. On the Color panel, check Fade Traces Over Time.

2. Using the **Line** tool, construct a horizontal line AB. The line should be about a third of the way from the bottom of the sketch window.

3. Use the **Segment** tool to construct segment CD where C is on the line and D is about an inch above it.

Click on an object with the **Text** tool to show its label. Double-click the label itself to change it.

4. Show the line's label and change it to *directrix*. Change point D's label to *D: focus*.

5. Construct the midpoint of segment CD by selecting it and choosing **Midpoint** from the Construct menu.

6. Select segment CD and midpoint E and choose **Perpendicular Line** from the Construct menu.

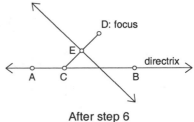

After step 6

The line you just constructed—perpendicular to segment CD through its midpoint—is called the perpendicular bisector *of segment CD.*

Q1 Imagine a point anywhere on the perpendicular bisector. How do you think the point's distance to *C* compares to its distance to *D*?

7. Construct a line perpendicular to $\overleftrightarrow{AB}$ and passing through point *C*.

8. Select the two perpendicular lines (the ones constructed in the last two steps) and choose **Intersection** from the Construct menu.

   You just constructed point F—the first point on the parabola.

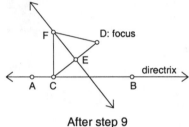

After step 9

*To hide objects, select them and choose **Hide** from the Display menu.*

9. Hide line *FC*. Then, using the **Segment** tool, construct segments *FC* and *FD*.

10. Measure the lengths of the two new segments. To do this, select them and choose **Length** from the Measure menu.

Q2 Using the **Arrow** tool, drag *C* back and forth along segment *AB*.

Refer back to the parabola definition in the Introduction.

What do you notice about the length measurements as you drag *C*? Explain how this demonstrates that *F* is indeed a point on the parabola defined by the given focus and directrix.

11. Select point *F* and choose **Trace Intersection** from the Display menu. Now once again drag *C* back and forth.

   Point F will leave a trail—called a trace—everywhere it goes.

12. Drag the focus away from the directrix. Again, drag point *C*. Notice how this curve compares to the previous one. Now drag the focus closer to the directrix than it was originally and repeat the process.

Tracing the curve in this way works well. But it can get a little annoying having to drag point *C* again and again. Here's a more efficient approach.

13. Select point *F* and choose **Trace Intersection** to turn off tracing for point *F*.

Parabolas: A Geometric Approach (continued)

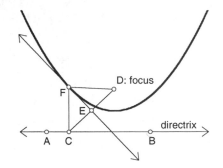

14. Select points *F* and *C* and choose **Locus** from the Construct menu.

    The entire curve appears. It's called the locus *of point F as point C moves along line AB.*

To hide objects, select them and choose **Hide** from the Display menu.

→15. To make the diagram less cluttered, hide everything except the parabola, the focus, and the directrix.

16. Drag the focus around and observe how the curve changes.

Q3 What happens to the parabola as the focus is dragged farther away from the directrix? Closer to it?

Q4 What happens to the parabola when the focus is dragged below the directrix?

17. Save your sketch. You may want to use it for the next activity, Building Headlights and Satellite Dishes.

Explore More

1. Use the commands in the Construct menu to construct the vertex of your parabola. This point should remain the vertex no matter where you drag the focus and the directrix.

2. Show that the equation of a parabola with its vertex at the origin and its focus at $(0, p)$ is $y = x^2/(4p)$. To do this, select the vertex you constructed in the previous Explore More and choose **Define Origin** from the Graph menu. Then measure the *y*-coordinate (*ordinate*) of the focus and relabel this measurement *p*. Now use **Plot New Function** from the Graph menu to plot $x^2/(4p)$. This plot should be right on top of the parabola, even if you drag the focus or the directrix.

Building Headlights and Satellite Dishes

Name(s): _____

Have you ever wondered why satellite dishes are shaped the way they are? And what is it about the way headlights are designed that makes the light travel outward in one direction? It turns out that both devices use *parabolic reflectors* because of their special reflective properties. In this activity, you'll construct a two-dimensional model of a parabolic reflector and explore what makes it ideal for reflecting and collecting rays.

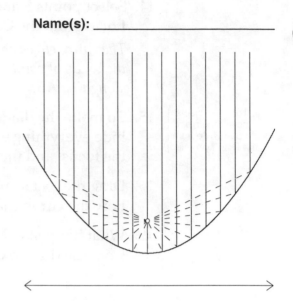

Background

In order for this activity to make sense, there are two things you need to know about the **Law of Reflection**. First, when a ray of light reflects off a flat surface, such as a mirror, the *angle of incidence* (∠1 below) equals the *angle of reflection* (∠2 below). This is a fancy-sounding law of physics that states something very simple—light bounces off at the same angle it hits. Second, if light bounces off a *curved* surface, the Law of Reflection still holds—just imagine the light bouncing off a line *tangent* to the curve.

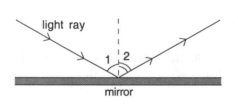

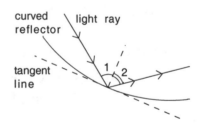

Sketch and Investigate

1. Open your sketch from the previous activity, Parabolas: A Geometric Approach, if you have it. Otherwise, open the sketch **Reflector.gsp** from the folder **3_Quads** and skip to step 4.

To hide objects, select them and choose **Hide** from the Display menu.

2. Choose **Show All Hidden** from the Display menu. Then hide all but the following objects: the parabola, focus, directrix, points *C* and *F*, and the line that's tangent to the parabola.

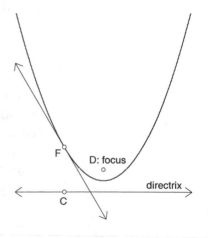

---

3. To make the parabola flatter, drag the directrix down near the bottom of the window and the focus about two-thirds of the way to the top.

4. Using the **Point** tool, draw a new point G inside the parabola somewhere between the focus and the vertex.

   We'll consider this point our "light source"—the tiny light bulb inside a headlight whose light bounces off the reflector into the outside world.

Either use the **Segment** tool or select the two points and choose **Segment** from the Construct menu. → 5. Construct a segment between points G and F.

   This represents one ray of light hitting, but not yet bouncing off, the reflector.

6. Select the new segment and point C and choose **Locus** from the Construct menu. With the locus selected, choose **Dashed** from the Line Weight submenu of the Display menu. With the locus still selected, choose **Properties** from the Edit menu. On the Plot panel, set the number of samples to 15.

   You'll see 15 rays coming from the light source and hitting the reflector.

7. Select point F and the line that's tangent to the parabola. Then choose **Perpendicular Line** from the Construct menu.

8. Double-click the new line to mark it as a mirror for reflection. Now select point G and choose **Reflect** from the Transform menu.

   The reflected image of point G, G′, appears.

9. Select, in order, point F and point G′. Then choose **Ray** from the Construct menu.

   This ray is the original ray of light after it's bounced off the reflector. By reflecting G across the perpendicular line, we guaranteed that the angle of incidence would equal the angle of reflection, as the Law of Reflection states.

10. Repeat step 6 using the new ray in place of the segment. Give the new locus a thin line weight (instead of dashed) to distinguish it from the other, and set the number of samples to 15 as well.

    You should now see the 15 rays of light coming from the light source and bouncing off the reflector.

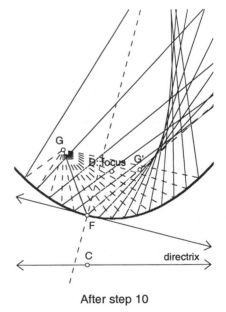

After step 10

Q1 Drag the light source around and observe how its location affects the reflected light. Where does the light source need to be in order for the light to travel out in parallel rays, as with car headlights?

11. Merge the light source and the focus. To do this, select these two points and choose **Merge Points** from the Edit menu.
The two points merge into one. Now the light source is at the focus and light is bouncing off in parallel rays.

12. Clean up the sketch by hiding segment *DF*, the perpendicular line through point *F*, the ray originating at *F*, the other point defining that ray, and anything else you'd like out of the way.

Q2 A satellite dish operates very differently from a car's headlights: Using one small sensor, it collects a bunch of electromagnetic rays coming in roughly parallel to each other. Explain how you would design a satellite dish.

Explore More

1. Do some research to find other objects shaped like a parabolic dish. Explain why each of them uses this shape.

Chapter 3: Parabolas and Quadratic Equations
Project Ideas

The projects below extend your knowledge of parabolas and quadratic equations and are suitable for in-class presentations, papers, or personal exploration.

1. Given any two points, it's possible to construct the unique line containing them. In fact, Sketchpad's **Line** tool does just that. How many points are required to define a unique parabola? If you have that number of points, can you arrange them in such a way that they *don't* define any parabola? Explore these questions. As an extra challenge, create a custom tool called **Parabola** that constructs a parabola when you click on the proper number of arbitrary points.

2. Make a *parabolic envelope* as follows: Mark a point *A* about 1 inch from the bottom of a blank piece of paper. As shown at right, fold the paper so that a point on the bottom edge lands directly onto point *A*. Make a sharp crease to keep a record of this fold, then unfold it. Fold the paper along a new crease so that a different point on the bottom edge lands on point *A*. Repeat the process many times. Eventually, the creases will outline a parabola.

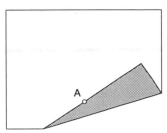

   Can you explain why this process works? Can you model this paper-folding technique in Sketchpad? See the activity The Folded Rectangle Construction from Key Curriculum Press' book *Exploring Conic Sections with The Geometer's Sketchpad* for more information.

3. In the Chapter 2 activity An Ant's Progress: Modeling Linear Motion in Time, you learned how to use parametric equations to model the steady motion of an ant across a piece of graph paper. In this chapter, you learned about parabolas. Combine these two topics by modeling the parabolic path of baseball with parametric equations. For some help, look up "projectile motion" in a math or physics textbook, or on the web.

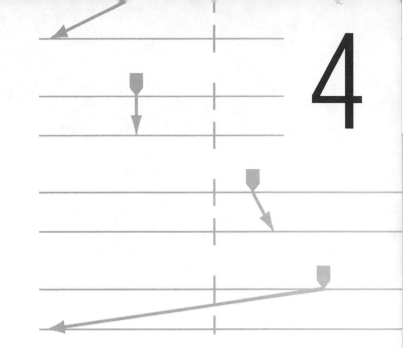

Functions

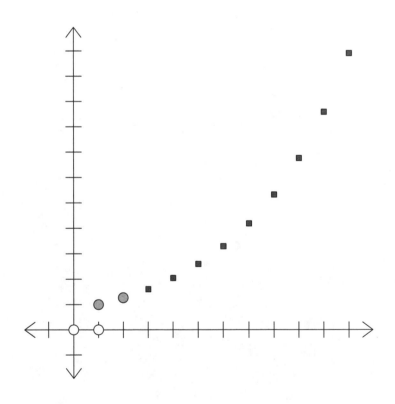

The Circumference Function

In a function, one quantity *depends* on another quantity just as the number of songs a jukebox plays depends on how much money is put in. We can say that a circle's circumference *depends* on its diameter—the farther it is across a circle, the farther it is around it. In this activity, you'll explore the diameter-circumference relationship in a way that may be new to you: as a *functional* relationship between two changing quantities.

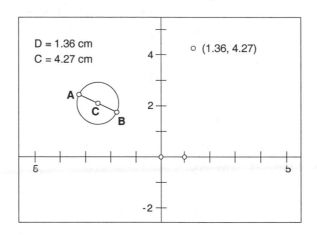

Imagine and Predict

Imagine doing the following (don't make any calculations or drawings):

> You use a compass to draw a circle. You measure the circle's diameter (3.5 inches) and calculate its circumference (about 11 inches). You then plot the point (3.5, 11) on a piece of graph paper. You draw a second circle, measure its diameter (*D*), calculate its circumference (*C*), and plot a second point (*D*, *C*). You do this for many more circles, each time plotting the point (*diameter of circle, circumference of circle*).

What will your graph look like after you plot many, many points?

Take a moment to think about this or discuss it in a group. Will the graph be a straight line or will it be a curve? Why? If it's a straight line, what will its slope be? If it's a curve, what shape will it be—will it bend upward or downward? Will the graph go on forever in both directions, or will it "start" or "stop" somewhere? Write or draw your prediction below.

The Circumference Function (continued)

Sketch and Investigate

You'll now test your prediction using Sketchpad.

The **Segment** tool

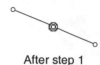

After step 1

→ 1. In a new sketch, use the **Segment** tool to construct a segment. With the segment selected, choose **Midpoint** from the Construct menu.

The **Compass** tool

→ 2. Construct a circle whose diameter is the segment. To do this, choose the **Compass** tool, click on the midpoint, then click on one of the endpoints.

Step 2

3. Measure the segment's length by selecting it and choosing **Length** from the Measure menu. Use a similar technique to measure the circle's circumference.

Double-click the measurements with the **Text** tool (the 'A' in the Toolbox) to edit their labels.

→ 4. Relabel the length measurement *D* (for diameter) and the circumference measurement *C*.

5. With the **Arrow** tool, select measurements *D* and *C* *in that order*. Then choose **Plot As (x, y)** from the Graph menu.

Sketchpad plots a point (D, C) whose x-coordinate is the diameter and whose y-coordinate the circumference of the circle. If you can't see the point yet, make the circle smaller.

6. Select the plotted point and choose **Trace Plotted Point** from the Display menu.

Q1 The moment of truth has arrived! Drag either one of the diameter's endpoints and observe the trace of the plotted point. Describe this trace below. Was your prediction correct?

Further Exploration

You've now seen the shape of the diameter-circumference trace. But why does it look the way it does? You may know that lines can be modeled with equations of the form $y = mx + b$ ($C = mD + b$ here). So what are *m* and *b* for this line? There's still a lot to explore.

Q2 Why does it make sense that the trace goes through the origin? What does this tell you about *m* and *b* in the equation $C = mD + b$?

Exploring Algebra with The Geometer's Sketchpad
© 2002 Key Curriculum Press

The Circumference Function (continued)

Q3 Choose **Snap Points** from the Graph menu. Now drag the diameter endpoints so that the diameter equals exactly 1.

What is the approximate circumference of a circle with diameter 1? Is this number familiar to you? If so, what's it called?

*Choose **Calculate** from the Measure menu to open the Calculator. Click on C and D in the sketch to enter them into the calculation.*

7. Choose **Snap Points** again to toggle grid-snapping off.

Q4 Use Sketchpad's Calculator to find the ratio C/D. Drag one of the diameter endpoints and observe the ratio. What happens and why?

*Select just the plotted point and choose **Trace Plotted Point** to toggle tracing off.*

8. Turn tracing off for your plotted point.

9. Construct a ray from the origin through the plotted point. Then measure the ray's slope.

Q5 What does the slope measurement tell you about m and b in $C = mD + b$?

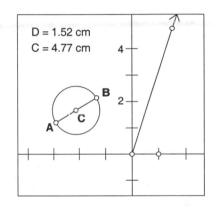

D = 1.52 cm
C = 4.77 cm

You've now seen the same number, π, represent three different things:

- the circumference of a circle with diameter 1
- the ratio of any circle's circumference to its diameter
- the slope of the graph of a circle's circumference as a function of its diameter

*Choose **Plot New Function** from the Graph menu and enter your proposed expression. Use x for the diameter (because you made D the x-coordinate earlier).*

Q6 Use what you learned in Q2 and Q5 to plot a line that includes the ray from step 10. Write the function you used below.

$f(x) =$

Explore More

1. What's an appropriate domain for the circumference function? Select the function plot from Q6 and choose **Properties** from the Edit menu. Go to the Plot panel and set an appropriate domain for this situation.

2. Consider a circle's *area* as a function of its radius. How will the plot of that function compare with the diameter-circumference plot? Make a prediction, then use the techniques from this activity to confirm.

Functions in a Triangle

Name(s):_____

In this activity, you'll construct a simple geometric figure, make two measurements, and observe how the measurements are related as the figure changes. This kind of relationship—where one quantity changes as a result of another quantity changing—is an example of a function.

Sketch

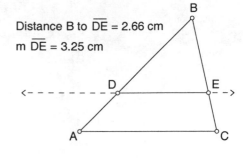

Distance B to $\overline{DE}$ = 2.66 cm

m $\overline{DE}$ = 3.25 cm

Choose **Preferences** *from the Edit menu and click on the Text tab.*

1. Open a new sketch. On the Text Preferences panel, check For All New Points.

   From now on, points will be labeled as they are created.

The **Segment** tool

2. Use the **Segment** tool to construct △*ABC*.

3. Using the **Point** tool, construct point *D* on side *AB*.

Select D and $\overline{AC}$; then choose **Parallel Line** *from the Construct menu.*

4. Construct a line through point *D* parallel to side *AC*.

5. Construct point *E* where this line intersects side *BC*. To do this, just click on the spot with the **Arrow** tool.

For the first measurement, select B and $\overline{DE}$; then choose **Distance** *from the Measure menu. For the second, select $\overline{DE}$ and choose* **Length**.

6. Hide the line and construct $\overline{DE}$. Measure the distance from point *B* to $\overline{DE}$. Then measure the length of $\overline{DE}$.

Investigate

You've now completed the basic setup. It's time to explore the relationship between the two measurements you've made.

7. Drag point *D* back and forth. Observe the measurements and think about how they relate to each other.

It's also possible, though perhaps less natural, to think of the distance from point B to $\overline{DE}$ as dependant on $\overline{DE}$'s length.

One way to think about this is that the length of $\overline{DE}$ depends on how far $\overline{DE}$ is from *B*. Considered that way, the length of $\overline{DE}$ is the dependent variable and the distance from *B* to $\overline{DE}$ is the independent variable.

Q1 On the axes at right, make a rough sketch of what a graph of the relationship might look like. Use the *x*-axis for the independent variable—the distance from *B* to $\overline{DE}$. Use the *y*-axis for the dependent variable—the length of $\overline{DE}$. Don't bother to scale the axes or to plot points of actual measurement values. Just test your intuition by drawing.

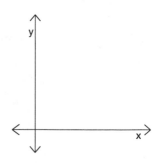

If you don't see the plotted point right away, make your triangle smaller or drag the unit point at (1, 0) to the left. | → 8. Select the two measurements—distance from B to $\overline{DE}$ and length of $\overline{DE}$—in that order. Choose **Plot As (x, y)** from the Graph menu.

You'll get a set of axes and a plotted point. Drag point D and observe the plotted point. Does its path correspond with the graph you sketched?

9. To see the set of all possible plotted points, select the plotted point and point D; then choose **Locus** from the Construct menu.

Q2 Describe the graph and explain what it illustrates about the functional relationship in the construction.

The *domain* of a function is the set of possible values for the independent variable. The *range* is the set of possible values for the dependent variable. | →**Q3** Describe the domain and range of this function. What do the maximum values of each correspond to in the construction?

10. Drag any vertex of the triangle to change the triangle's shape and size. Observe how this affects the graph.

Q4 Describe the different types of graphs you get with different kinds of triangles. For example, what shapes give graphs with steeper slopes? Less steep slopes?

Explore More

With the New Function dialog box open, click on the measurements in the sketch to enter them into the function equation. | → 1. Use the **Plot New Function** command (and the measurements in the sketch) to plot a function that coincides with your locus graph.

2. How do you think the plots of length $\overline{BD}$ versus length $\overline{DE}$ or length $\overline{BE}$ versus length $\overline{DE}$ would compare to your existing plot? Make a prediction. Then test it by constructing segments BD and BE, measuring their lengths, and constructing the loci as you did before.

3. Make other measurements in the construction and investigate other functional relationships. See if you can find one that's not linear.

Functional Geometry

Name(s): _____

In many geometric situations, one aspect or quantity in a figure *depends on* another aspect or quantity. For example, as the diameter of a circle grows, the circumference grows as well—the circumference can be thought of as depending on the diameter. This is an example of a functional relationship. The diameter is the independent variable, x, and the circumference is the dependent variable, y or $f(x)$.

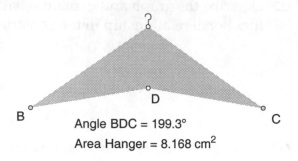

Angle BDC = 199.3°
Area Hanger = 8.168 cm^2

Sketch and Investigate

What you'll do with the last two pages, Hanger and View Tube, will be a little different. But by the time you get there, it should be clear what to do.

1. Open the sketch **Geometric Functions.gsp** from the folder **4_Functions**.

   This multi-page document has nine pages of different geometric figures. On each page, your task is to find and explore functional relationships. The first page is a circle with a diameter, as described above. You can start here for practice, or you can skip to the next page if the circle function is already familiar. With each page, do each of the following steps (2–8).

2. Familiarize yourself with the figure by dragging. (In particular, drag point D.) Then choose two things of interest to measure in the sketch. Measure them, then drag some more to get a first taste of how the two measurements relate.

   On the Circle page, you would probably measure the length of the diameter and either the circumference or the area of the circle.

3. Decide which of the things you measured depends on the other. That will be your dependent variable, y. The other will be your independent variable, x. (You can usually choose either way, as long as you're aware of how you're thinking about the relationship when you graph it.)

4. On graph paper, make a guess at what the graph of the relationship will look like. Try to do this just from your observations of the changing figure as you drag.

Exploring Algebra with The Geometer's Sketchpad
© 2002 Key Curriculum Press

If the plotted point isn't visible, rescale the axes by dragging the unit point at (1, 0) to the left. → 5. To test your guess, select the two measurements in the following order: the independent variable (x) then the dependent variable (y). Choose **Plot As (x, y)** from the Graph menu.

A pair of axes and the plotted point will appear.

6. Drag point D again and observe the path of the plotted point.

7. To actually see the graph of the plotted point, select it and point D and choose **Locus** from the Construct menu.

8. On your graph paper, sketch the actual graph and compare it to your guess.

Some Function Suggestions

Page	Suggestions
Circle	(*diameter, circumference*)
Triangle	(*AD, DE*) or (*distance A to DE, DE*)
Xquad	(*AD, DE*)
Rect 1	(*AD, AB*) or (*AD, perimeter*) or (*AD, area*)
Rect 2	(*AD, AB*) or (*AD, perimeter*) or (*AD, area*)
Polygons	(*AD, area*) or (*AD, perimeter*) for each polygon (and compare graphs)
Ladder	(*AD, AB*)
Hanger	(*angle, area*)
Tube View	(*tube length* or *tube diameter* or *distance, field of view*)

Explore More

1. See if you can write an equation for one or more of the functional relationships you graphed. Plot that function (using **Plot New Function** in the Graph menu) to see if it matches the locus graph. (You might need to measure things in the sketch to use as parameters in your function.)

Representing Functions Dynamically: Introducing Dynagraphs

Name(s): _____

How many ways are there to represent a function?

Perhaps you've encountered *verbal* representations of functions or functions presented as *arrows* connecting the elements of two sets. You may have seen them displayed using *tables* or even *equations*. Here we explore a useful new way of representing functions: *dynagraphs*.

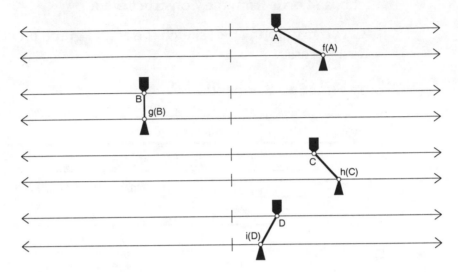

Sketch and Explore

Q1 Spend a few moments reviewing with your group or on your own what a *function* is.

Based on what you've learned so far in your math life, how would you describe functions to someone who isn't familiar with them?

1. Open the sketch **Dynagraphs.gsp** from the folder **4_Functions**.

   You'll see four dynagraphs. Each consists of two axes: an input axis and an output axis. Segments connect points on the input axes to points on the output axes.

2. Using the **Arrow** tool, drag each of the four input pointers (pentagons) to get an idea of how dynagraphs work.

Q2 Based on your understanding of functions, do these four dynagraphs represent functions? Explain.

Q3 Here's a description of dynagraph *f*:

> When the input is at the origin, the output is also at the origin. When the input is right of the origin, so is the output, but the output is always about twice as far away. When the input is on the left side, it's a mirror image of when it's on the right. When the input is dragged steadily from left to right, the output also moves steadily in the same direction, only faster.

You don't have to copy what's in our description. Just be as observant and detailed as you can. You might imagine you're describing the dynagraphs to someone who can't see them. →

Write descriptions for the other three dynagraphs.

Dynagraph *g* description:

Dynagraph *h* description:

Dynagraph *i* description:

Numbers, Numbers, Numbers

You may have suspected (correctly) that the input and output axes in a dynagraph are number lines. But without any tick marks other than the origin, it's impossible to assign numbers to positions, such as "an input of 3 gives an output of 5."

In this section, you'll explore four new dynagraphs, first without numbers, then with.

3. Go to page 2 of **Dynagraphs.gsp**. You'll see four new dynagraphs. Explore them by dragging their input pointers.

Q4 On a separate piece of paper, write descriptions of the four functions represented by these dynagraphs, just as in the previous section.

4. Scroll down a bit and press the *Show axes* button.

   You now see that the dynagraphs' axes are indeed number lines.

5. Drag *t*'s input control to 4.

   The arrow should point to an output of 5, as shown at right. Thus, an input of 4 maps to an output of 5. Using functional notation, t(4) = 5, or "t of four equals five."

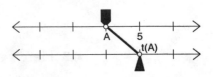

Hint: The answers to all but three of these questions are single integers. The answer to one question is "undefined," and one question has several answers.

Q5 Solve for the unknown as indicated.

$t(1) = y, \quad y =$ $\qquad$ $v(4) = b, \quad b =$

$t(5) = n, \quad n =$ $\qquad$ $v(-4) = d, \quad d =$

$t(x) = -5, \quad x =$ $\qquad$ $v(r) = 3, \quad r =$

$u(-1) = ?, \quad ? =$ $\qquad$ $w(2) = z, \quad z =$

$u(3) = p, \quad p =$ $\qquad$ $w(4) = s, \quad s =$

$u(m) = 8, \quad m =$ $\qquad$ $w(a) = 0, \quad a =$

Explore More—Absolute Maximums and Minimums

A function is said to have an *absolute maximum* if there is a "biggest" output value—one the function can take on but can never exceed. Similarly, a function is said to have an *absolute minimum* if there is a "smallest" output value—one the function can take on but can never go below.

1. Of the eight functions on pages 1 and 2, one has an absolute maximum and two have absolute minimums. Determine which functions these are. Also determine what the maximum/minimum output values are and for what input values they occur.

From Dynagraphs to Cartesian Graphs

Name(s): _____

In the previous activity, you saw how useful dynagraphs can be for representing and understanding functions. The problem is, you may not see too many dynagraphs in your future math studies; Cartesian graphs (those in the *x-y* plane) are much more common. In this activity, we'll combine the best of both worlds by gradually transforming dynagraphs into their Cartesian counterparts.

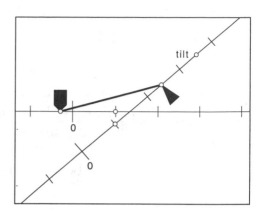

Function Matchmaking

Let's start out with some "function matchmaking" to get your feet wet. Specifically, you'll match several dynagraphs to their corresponding algebraic equations.

Since neither line contains numbers, you'll need to be as observant as possible. How does the input pointer move in relation to the output pointer?

Q1 Open the sketch **DynaToCart.gsp** from the folder **4_Functions**. You'll see several dynagraphs, numbered 1–5. Each dynagraph can be matched to an equation below. Pair each dynagraph with its corresponding function and explain how you made the match.

a. $y = x$

b. $y = -x$

c. $y = 2x$

d. $y = x^2$

e. $y = \dfrac{1}{x-1} + 1$

From Dynagraphs to Cartesian Graphs

1. Go to page 2 of **DynaToCart.gsp**.

   You'll see a dynagraph for the function $f(x) = 2x - 1$. Drag the input pointer to familiarize yourself with this function.

2. Drag the point labeled *tilt* so that the output axis is at an angle to the input axis. Drag the input pointer again. Do this for a few different angles of the output axis. (You can even turn it upside down!)

Q2 What changes and what remains the same after tilting the output axis?

The major difference between dynagraphs and Cartesian (*x-y*) graphs is this: With dynagraphs, one point represents the input value and a second point represents the output value; with Cartesian graphs, one point represents *both* the input and output values. To see how this could be, continue on.

3. Press the *Make Cartesian* button and watch as the two axes of your dynagraph "morph" into the familiar *x*- and *y*-axes. Drag the input pointer once more to remind yourself that you're still dealing with the same dynagraph, only tilted.

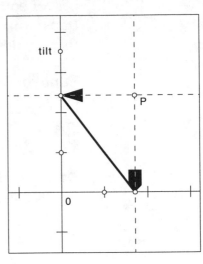

4. Press the *Show Perpendiculars* button to show lines through *A* and *f*(*A*) perpendicular to the two axes.

Simply click at the proper spot to construct the intersection. → 5. Construct the point of intersection of the two perpendiculars.

6. With the new point selected, measure its coordinates by choosing **Coordinates** from the Measure menu.

Q3 What does the *x*-coordinate of the new point correspond to on the dynagraph? How about its *y*-coordinate?

7. Deselect all objects by clicking in blank space. Select the new point and choose **Trace Intersection** from the Display menu. Now drag the input pointer and watch as *P* traces out the graph of *f*(*x*).

Q4 Describe the shape of the graph traced by the intersection point. Why does this shape makes sense given the behavior of the dynagraph.

Simultaneous Representation

8. Go to page 3 of **DynaToCart.gsp**.

   You'll see a dynagraph and a Cartesian graph, both modeling $f(x) = 2x - 1$. Drag the input pointer on the dynagraph and watch both models change simultaneously.

Q5 A classmate says, "One Cartesian point contains the same information as two dynagraph points." Explain what she means.

Double-click the function equation $f(x) = 2 \cdot x - 1$ to edit it.

9. Explore each of the following functions on the dynagraph/Cartesian graph. In each case, start with the input pointer toward the left and drag it slowly from left to right.

   $f(x) = 3$ $\qquad\qquad$ $f(x) = x$ $\qquad\qquad$ $f(x) = -x$

   $f(x) = x^2$ $\qquad\qquad$ $f(x) = -x^2$ $\qquad\qquad$ $f(x) = 5x$

Q6 Fill in the blanks.

When the input and output pointers both move right, the Cartesian point moves _____.

When the input pointer moves right and the output pointer moves left, the Cartesian point moves _____.

Q7 How does the Cartesian graph of $f(x) = 5x$ compare to that of $f(x) = x$? How does this relate to the difference between their dynagraphs?

Q8 In what ways do you think dynagraphs are better for representing functions than Cartesian graphs? In what ways are Cartesian graphs better for representing functions than dynagraphs?

Exploring Domain and Range with Dynagraphs and Cartesian Graphs

Name(s): _____

You can't put a television in a blender and you wouldn't expect an elephant to come out of a gasoline pump. In math terms, a television isn't an *allowable input* for a blender; it's not part of a blender's *domain*. And an elephant isn't a *possible output* of a gasoline pump; it's not part of a gas pump's *range*.

Similarly, functions have certain numbers that are and aren't allowed as inputs, and other numbers that are and aren't possible as outputs. In this activity, you'll explore these notions using both dynagraphs and Cartesian graphs.

Sketch and Investigate

The *range* of a function is the set of possible outputs from that function. Let's see how dynagraphs can make this idea clearer. You'll start by exploring the range of everyone's favorite dynagraph: the "blue hopper."

1. Open the sketch **Domain Range.gsp** from the folder **4_Functions**. Drag the input pointer to refamiliarize yourself with $f(x) = \text{round}(x)$.

2. Select the output pointer (triangle) and choose **Trace Triangle** from the Display menu. Now drag the input pointer back and forth.

The output pointer leaves a *trace* of where it's been. Since the traces point to all the integers and never to any non-integer value, we say that "the range of f is all integers."

The answer to each of these will either be "all real numbers" or an inequality such as $f(x) \geq 5$.

Q1 Go to page 2 of **Domain Range.gsp**. Use the technique from step 2 to find the ranges of the four functions modeled.

$g(x)$: $h(x)$:

$i(x)$: $j(x)$:

When using technology, it's very important to know the *limitations* of that technology. You'll now see that the method used above can be misleading in certain situations. You'll then learn a more reliable method.

3. Go to page 3 of **Domain Range.gsp**. Turn tracing on for the output pointer, then drag the input pointer, as in step 2. For greater control, use the right and left arrow keys on your keyboard to drag one pixel (screen unit) at a time.

Q2 What does the range of $k(x) = 20 \cdot x$ *appear* to be? Explain why this answer is actually wrong! Why do you think this happens?

4. Select the input pointer and choose **Animate Pentagon** from the Display menu. Repeatedly press the Decrease Speed button (the down arrow) on the Motion Controller until it's clear that the range of this function really is all real numbers.

   You may also want to go back to pages 1 and 2 of the sketch and convince yourself that your answers there were correct.

The *domain* of a function is the set of allowable inputs into that function—the set of inputs that produce meaningful outputs. For most functions you'll study this year, the domain will be "all real numbers," meaning that any input (3, 0, –58 billion, 1.7924, or whatever) produces some output.

Sometimes, however, a domain might be *restricted* to be something such as "all integers" or "$x > 3$." In the first case, only integer inputs produce outputs; in the second, only real numbers greater than 3 produce outputs.

5. Go to page 4 of **Domain Range.gsp**.

Q3 Drag v's input pointer back and forth. What is v's domain? (In other words, where can you drag the input pointer and still see the output pointer?) What is v's range?

Q4 Why, based on its equation, are some numbers not part of v's domain?

Q5 The domain of w is all real numbers except for one particular value. The range of w is also all real numbers except for one particular value (a different value). What is the one value not in the domain of w? What is the one value not in the range of w?

Exploring Domain and Range (continued)

Domain and Range on Cartesian Graphs

Dynagraphs are great for learning things about functions, but it's important to transfer this knowledge to Cartesian graphs since they're much more common.

The "round" function has a page of its own because it needs a special setting in order to display properly in the Cartesian plane.

→ 5. Go to page 5 of **Domain Range.gsp**.

You'll see that it's set up with the rounding function. Drag the input pointer and think about how you can tell domain and range on a Cartesian graph.

To change the function represented, double-click the function equation for f(x).

→ 6. Go to page 6 of **Domain Range.gsp** and explore the function $f(x) = 2x$. Explore the rest of the functions from page 2 here, again thinking about how to tell domain and range on a Cartesian graph.

Q6 How can you tell the range of a function just by looking at its Cartesian graph? How about its domain?

Explore More

1. Go back to page 1 of **Domain Range.gsp**. How can you change f's equation so that its range is all even numbers? All odd numbers? On page 3, how can you change v so that both its domain and range are all numbers *less than* or equal to 0? How can you change w so that its *domain* is all real numbers except 0 and its *range* is all real numbers except 2.

Exploring Odd and Even Functions with Dynagraphs and Cartesian Graphs

Name(s): _____

Just as there are odd and even numbers, there are odd and even functions. As you'll see, whether a function is odd, even, or neither depends on whether it exhibits certain kinds of symmetry. In this activity, you'll explore these symmetries on both dynagraphs and Cartesian graphs.

Sketch and Investigate

1. Open the sketch **Odd Even.gsp** from the folder **4_Functions**.

Q1 On the first dynagraph, compare $f(2)$ with $f(-2)$. Then compare $f(-1)$ with $f(1)$, $f(3)$ with $f(-3)$, and $f(-0.5)$ with $f(0.5)$. In each case, what do you notice about how $f(A)$ compares with $f(-A)$?

Functions like this, where the output for an input x is the *opposite* of the output for $-x$, are said to be *odd* or have *odd symmetry*. We can say:

An *odd function* is one in which $f(-x) = -f(x)$ for all x in its domain.

Q2 Of the other three functions modeled on page 1 of **Odd Even.gsp**, which are odd?

2. Go to page 2 of **Odd Even.gsp**.

Q3 On the first dynagraph, compare $t(2)$ with $t(-2)$. Then compare $t(-1)$ with $t(1)$, $t(3)$ with $t(-3)$, and $t(-0.5)$ with $t(0.5)$. In each case, what do you notice about how $t(A)$ compares with $t(-A)$?

Functions like this, where the output for an input x is the *same* as the output for $-x$, are said to be *even* or have *even symmetry*. We can say:

An *even function* is one in which $f(-x) = f(x)$ for all x in its domain.

Exploring Odd and Even Functions (continued)

Q4 Of the other three functions modeled on page 2 of **Odd Even.gsp**, which are even?

Q5 Describe how you can tell if a dynagraph you're exploring represents an odd or an even function just by dragging (in other words, without looking at its equation).

Don't worry if you're not familiar with the sine or cosine functions—you can tell if they're odd or even just as with the other functions. To enter "sin" or "cos" in the Edit Function dialog box, use the Functions pop-up menu.

Q6 Go to page 3 of **Odd Even.gsp**. Model the three odd functions from page 1 and the three even functions from page 2 on the combination dynagraph/Cartesian graph. What do odd functions look like when plotted in the x-y plane? How about even functions?

Q7 Model the functions below on the combination dynagraph/Cartesian graph. Some of the functions are odd, some are even, and one is neither. Use what you learned in Q6 to determine which are which (in other words, don't use the dynagraph).

$$f(x) = 5x \qquad f(x) = x^2 + 2 \qquad f(x) = x^3 - 2x$$

$$f(x) = x^4 - 3x^3 \qquad f(x) = \sin(x) \qquad f(x) = \cos(x)$$

Explore More

1. Why are odd functions called "odd" and even functions called "even?" You may be able to figure this out by looking at the equations of the odd and even functions you've seen in this activity. (*Hint:* Focus on just the polynomial equations.) Test your answer by modeling your own odd and even functions in Sketchpad and checking that they exhibit the proper symmetry.

2. Imagine that both $f(x)$ and $g(x)$ are odd functions. What kind of function will $(f + g)(x)$ be? What about $(f \cdot g)(x)$? What about $f(g(x))$? What would the answer to these questions be if f and g were both even? What if one were even and the other odd?

Exploring Algebra with The Geometer's Sketchpad
© 2002 Key Curriculum Press

Exploring Function Composition with Dynagraphs

Name(s): _____

In life, the answer to one question sometimes becomes a question that leads to another answer. Functions are much the same; sometimes we take the output of one function and make it the input for a second function. This is called *function composition*. In this activity, you'll get a brief introduction to function composition and then see how dynagraphs can provide a compelling way of modeling composed functions.

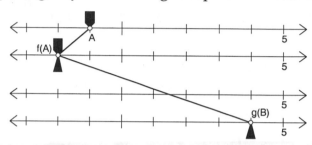

Introduction

We'll introduce function composition informally by doing an example:

> The composite function $g(f(3))$ is pronounced "*g* of *f* of 3."

Given $f(x) = 2x$ and $g(x) = x^2$, find $g(f(3))$.

- Start on the inside by evaluating $f(3)$: $f(3) = 2 \cdot 3 = 6$
- Take this output and make it g's input: $g(f(3)) = g(6) = 6^2 = 36$

That, in a tiny nutshell, is function composition!

Q1 Given the functions

$$f(x) = 2x, \quad g(x) = x^2, \quad h(x) = \text{round}(x), \quad \text{and } i(x) = x/2,$$

evaluate the following expressions.

a. $g(f(5)) =$ b. $f(g(3)) =$ c. $f(h(3.6)) =$

d. $i(g(-6)) =$ e. $i(f(17)) =$ f. $f(i(17)) =$

Q2 Do you think $f(g(x))$ always equals $g(f(x))$? Answer this question by comparing $f(g(5))$ and $g(f(5))$.

Sketch and Investigate

1. Open the sketch **Composition.gsp** from the folder **4_Functions**. Drag both input pointers (pentagons) to familiarize yourself with the dynagraphs of functions f and g.

Exploring Function Composition with Dynagraphs (continued)

You'll now model $g(f(x))$. The trick is using Sketchpad's **Split** and **Merge** commands to make the output of f become the input of g.

2. Select point B (at the tip of g's input pointer) and choose **Split Point From Axis** from the Edit menu.

   The point detaches from its axis.

3. Select points B and $f(A)$ and choose **Merge Points** from the Edit menu.

   The two points merge into one—f's output is now g's input! Drag f's input pointer to explore your new composite function, $g(f(x))$, and to check your answer from Q1a.

4. While holding down the Shift key, choose **Undo All** from the Edit menu. Now use the technique from steps 2 and 3 to model $f(g(x))$.

   Q3 Use your composite dynagraph to evaluate these expressions.

   a. $f(g(1)) =$ b. $f(g(-1)) =$ c. $f(g(-7)) =$

Next, you'll compose the "round" and "square" functions to create a composite function with an interesting set of outputs.

   Q4 Go to page "g & h" and model $g(h(x))$. What is the range of this composite function? (In other words, what are its possible outputs?)

Composition.gsp contains duplicates of each page, so you can construct both of these composite dynagraphs at once.

   → **Q5** Create the composite functions $i(f(x))$ and $f(i(x))$ on the appropriate pages. Experiment with these functions. What special feature do you notice about these two composite functions? Why does this happen?

Explore More

1. There's nothing stopping you from composing more than two functions to get something such as $h(g(f(x)))$. Go to page "all 4" and try this for different combinations of three or four functions. See if you can build the following functions.

   a. a function that outputs twice perfect squares $(0, 2, 8, 18, \ldots)$

   b. a function that outputs squares of even numbers $(0, 4, 16, 36, \ldots)$

   c. a function that outputs one-fourth of perfect squares $(0, 0.25, 1, 4, 6.25, \ldots)$

Exploring Algebra with The Geometer's Sketchpad
© 2002 Key Curriculum Press

Thinking Differently: Again and Again   Name(s): _____

Imagine you have a long piece of licorice you want to split into eight equal pieces to share with seven friends. First, you break the licorice in half; then you break the halves in half; and finally, you break the smaller pieces in half for a total of eight equal-sized pieces.

Mathematicians use a fancy word for repeating a process over and over again: *iteration*. In the situation described above, you took an object—the licorice—and *iterated* an operation on that object: breaking the piece(s) in half. Of course, mathematicians like to iterate other operations too. In this activity, you'll iterate arithmetic operations on the coordinates of points.

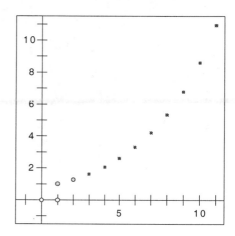

Imagine and Predict

Imagine doing the following (don't make any calculations or drawings):

> Choose a point in the *x-y* coordinate plane. Now add 1 to the *x*- and *y*-coordinates of that point to create the *x*- and *y*-coordinates of a new point. Then add 1 to the *x*- and *y*-coordinates of the new point to get a newer point. Keep iterating—that is, keep creating new points by adding 1 to each coordinate of the previous point.

What can you say about the points you get? Take a moment to think about this or discuss it in a group. Again, try to use only your imagination. If you drew lines between each successive point, what shape would you get? Write or draw your prediction below.

Sketch and Investigate

You'll now test your prediction using Sketchpad.

1. In a new sketch, choose **Define Coordinate System** from the Graph menu. Drag the unit point—the point at (1, 0)—toward the origin until the *x*-axis goes from about –50 to 50 units.

2. Use the **Point** tool to draw a point anywhere in the plane. Measure the *x*- and *y*-coordinates of the point using the **Abscissa (x)** and **Ordinate (y)** commands from the Measure menu.

   The point is assigned the label A and the measurements x_A and y_A appear.

   You'll now define the process of adding 1 to both the *x*- and *y*-coordinates.

Choose **Calculate** from the Measure menu to open the Calculator. Click on the measurements in the sketch to enter them into the calculation.

3. Use Sketchpad's Calculator to calculate $x_A + 1$. Then calculate $y_A + 1$.

   These operations calculate the coordinates of your new point.

4. Use the **Arrow** tool to select the new *x*-coordinate ($x_A + 1$) and the new *y*-coordinate ($y_A + 1$) *in that order.* Then choose **Plot As (x, y)** from the Graph menu to plot your new point.

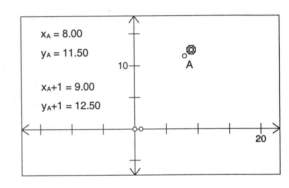

Select the two measurements and choose **Hide Measurements** from the Display menu.

5. Hide the x_A and y_A coordinate measurements.

Now you will use the **Iterate** command to create a bunch more points.

6. Select point *A* and choose **Iterate** from the Transform menu. You'll get a dialog box that asks you to map point *A* to another object. As shown below, click on the point you plotted in step 4 to map *A* to that point.

   In the sketch itself, Sketchpad plots several more points by repeating— iterating—the operation that maps point A to point B. Sketchpad also creates a table showing the calculations for each iterated point.

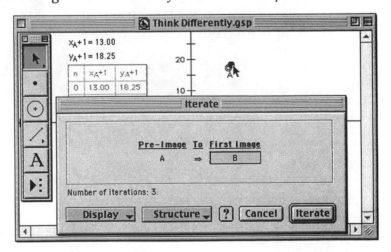

Exploring Algebra with The Geometer's Sketchpad
© 2002 Key Curriculum Press

Press the + key on your keyboard as a shortcut for **Increase Iterations**.

7. Choose **Increase Iterations** from the Display pop-up menu a few times to create more points and more table entries. Click Iterate to close the dialog box.

Q1 The moment of truth has arrived! Drag your initial point A around. How would you describe the sequence of iterated images generated by this iteration?

Q2 As you drag point A, what happens to the values in the table? What changes and what stays the same?

Q3 Imagine a line through your iterated sequence of points. What is the slope of this line?

Now let's change the iteration rule by changing the way new y-coordinates are generated. Instead of adding 1 to the y-coordinate, what if you were to add 4 or –3?

Q4 Change the rule $(y_A + 1)$ to $(y_A + 4)$ or $(y_A - 3)$. (Double-click the equation, then change the expression in the Calculator.) How do these changes affect both the table and the slope of the imaginary line?

8. You can also change the iteration rule by changing the way you generate new x-coordinates. Try adding 2 to the x-coordinate or even subtracting 0.5. Can you explain what happens?

Q5 What other combinations of n and m in the iteration rules $(x_A + n)$ and $(y_A + m)$ give the same slope you found in Q2?

When you've done this, you might try challenging your classmates to match a linear equation of your own choosing.

Q6 Use **Plot New Function** from the Graph menu to plot the equation $y = 3x + 2$. Can you match your iteration to this plot by changing the starting position and the operations that generate new x- and y-coordinates? Describe how you did this.

Explore More

So far you've generated only linear sequences, but there are many other types of sequences you can generate with this simple iteration rule. Some look quite strange, and some look like functions you're already familiar with.

You may want to increase the number of iterations for this investigation. To do this, select the iteration (by clicking on one of its points) and press the + key on your keyboard.

1. Instead of adding values to the y-coordinate of point A, you could multiply it by some value. For example, instead of using the rule $(y_A + 1)$, you could try $2 \cdot y_A$. (For now, keep adding 1 to the x-coordinate.) We can express this iteration rule like this: $(x_{new}, y_{new}) = (x_{old} + 1, 2 \cdot y_{old})$. How would you describe the iterated points now? Drag the starting point around. What effect does this seem to have? You might also want to investigate the family of iterations represented by $(x_{new}, y_{new}) = (x_{old} + 1, \ 2 \cdot y_{old} + k)$.

2. Another interesting variation to try is reversing the coordinates. For example, you could let your new x-coordinate be the same as the old y-coordinate and make your new y-coordinate be 1 more than the old x-coordinate. We could express this new iteration rule as: $(x_{new}, y_{new}) = (y_{old}, x_{old} + 1)$. How would you describe this sequence mathematically?

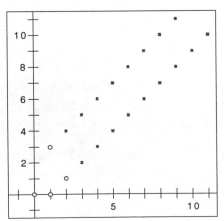

Chapter 4: Functions
Project Ideas

The projects below extend your knowledge of functions and are suitable for in-class presentations, papers, or personal exploration.

1. In Exploring Function Composition with Dynagraphs, you learned how to use dynagraphs to model composite functions. How would this work with Cartesian graphs? To find out, open the sketch **CartComp.gsp** from the folder **4_Functions** and follow the directions.

2. In Exploring Function Composition with Dynagraphs (specifically, Q2 and Q5), you saw that for some functions f and g, $f(g(x))$ always equals $g(f(x))$, while for some it doesn't. Do some research and find out what functions f and g are called if $f(g(x))$ does equal $g(f(x))$ for all values of x. What do these pairs of functions look like when modeled using Dynagraphs? Plotted in the Cartesian plane?

3. One of the best known iteration rules in mathematics produces the famous Fibonacci sequence: 1, 1, 2, 3, 5, 8, 13, 21, . . . Each term in the sequence (after the second) is the sum of the two preceding terms. This sequence was discovered many centuries ago and it shows up in many different areas of mathematics and the natural world.

   You can look at this sequence in terms of coordinates, taking each adjacent pair of terms as the coordinates of a point: (1, 1), (1, 2), (2, 3), (3, 5), (5, 8), . . . Can you adjust your iteration rule from Thinking Differently: Again and Again to produce these points? What shape does this sequence of points yield on the graph? How does this shape vary when you move the starting point? Can you find other ways of representing the Fibonacci sequence in Sketchpad?

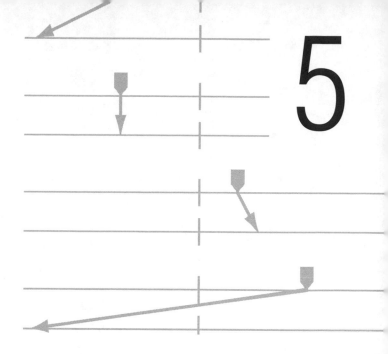

Transformations
and Vectors

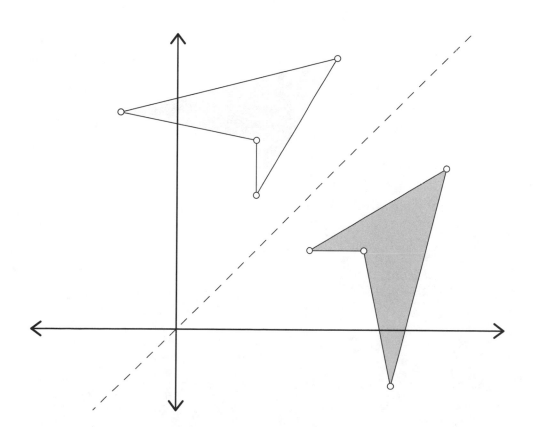

Translation in the Coordinate Plane

Name(s): _____

Analytic Geometry is a branch of mathematics defined as "the algebraic study of geometry by use of coordinate systems." In this activity, you'll do some Analytic Geometry as you study what happens to the coordinates of points—specifically, the vertices of a triangle—when they're translated.

Sketch

You'll start by creating a coordinate system and drawing the triangle to be translated.

Choose **Define Coordinate System** from the Graph menu. Then choose **Snap Points**.

→ 1. In a new sketch, create a new coordinate system with point snapping turned on.

2. Using the **Segment** tool, draw a triangle whose vertices are grid points.

Select the three points with the **Arrow** tool; then choose **Coordinates** from the Measure menu.

→ 3. Measure the coordinates of the triangle's three vertices.

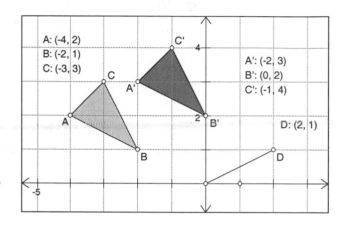

The points are given labels, A–C, and their coordinates are displayed.

4. Construct the triangle's interior. To do this, select its three vertices and choose **Triangle Interior** from the Construct menu.

Now you need to tell Sketchpad how to translate the triangle. To do this, you'll construct a segment and use it to define a *translation vector*.

5. Draw a segment from the origin to any grid point in the plane.

6. Measure the coordinates of the segment's "unattached" endpoint (not the origin).

Drag this new coordinate measurement so that it's away from the others.

Select, in order, the origin and point *A*; then choose **Mark Vector** from the Transform menu.

→ 7. Mark the vector from the origin to point *D*.

A brief animation indicates that a translation vector has been marked. A vector is a distance and a direction, such as "5 miles due east" or, in this case, "the distance and direction from the origin to point D."

Select the entire triangle (vertices, segments, and interior); then choose **Translate** from the Transform menu.

→ 8. Translate the triangle by the marked vector.

An "image" triangle appears.

9. Measure the coordinates of the new triangle's vertices.

10. Experiment by dragging point *D* or any of the triangle vertices. Look for a relationship between a point's coordinates, the coordinates of its image under a translation, and the coordinates of point *D*.

Investigate

Q1 Where can you drag point D so that the original points and their corresponding image points always have the same y-coordinates? The same x-coordinates?

Q2 When the vector you defined translates the triangle to the left and up, what must be true of the coordinates of point D?

Q3 Suppose point D has coordinates (s, t). What are the coordinates of the image of a point (x, y) under a translation by (s, t)?

Q4 Quadrilateral $JKLM$ has vertices J: $(-2, -1)$, K: $(-3, 3)$, L: $(-1, 1)$, and M: $(1, 2)$. In its translated image $J'K'L'M'$, J' is at $(1, -2)$, K' is at $(0, 2)$, and L' is at $(2, 0)$. Where is M'?

Q5 In the previous problem, assume that $JKLM$ was translated to $J'K'L'M'$ using the vector in the sketch. What are the coordinates of point D?

Explore More

1. Using Sketchpad's Measure menu, you can measure a point's *coordinates*, a segment's *slope* and *length*, and an interior's *perimeter* and *area*. Which of these measurements are preserved (don't change) under a translation? Which aren't?

2. Triangle UVW has vertices U: $(5, 8)$, V: $(2, -5)$, and W: $(-1, 3)$. Triangle XYZ has vertices X: $(3, 6)$, Y: $(0, -7)$, and Z: $(-2, 0)$. Explain why XYZ couldn't be the image of UVW under a translation.

Rotation in the Coordinate Plane

Name(s): _____

In this activity, you'll investigate what happens to the coordinates of points after you rotate them about the origin, mainly by multiples of 90°. If you do the Explore More exercises, you'll get to experiment with a new type of coordinate system: a *polar coordinate system*.

Sketch and Investigate

Choose **Define Coordinate System** from the Graph menu. Then choose **Snap Points**.

1. In a new sketch, create a new coordinate system with point snapping turned on.

2. Using the **Segment** tool, draw a quadrilateral whose vertices are grid points.

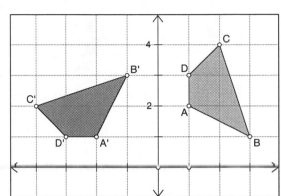

Select the four points with the **Arrow** tool; then choose **Coordinates** from the Measure menu.

3. Measure the coordinates of the four vertices.

   The points are given labels, A–D, and their coordinates are displayed.

4. Construct the quadrilateral's interior. To do this, select its four vertices consecutively clockwise or counterclockwise and choose **Quadrilateral Interior** from the Construct menu.

5. Mark the origin of your coordinate system as a center of rotation by double-clicking it.

Select the vertices, sides, and interior of the quadrilateral; then choose **Rotate** from the Transform menu, enter 90 for the angle, and click Rotate.

6. Rotate *ABCD* about the origin by 90°. Then drag a vertex of your original quadrilateral and observe the results.

7. Now rotate the image quadrilateral by 90°. Continue rotating each successive image quadrilateral by 90°. What eventually happens?

8. Measure the coordinates of vertex *A* and its three rotated images (its *corresponding* points on the other three quadrilaterals).

Q1 What is the relationship between the coordinates of a point and the coordinates of its image point after a 90° rotation about the origin?

Q2 Suppose that a point with coordinates (*a*, *b*) is rotated by 90° about the origin. What are the coordinates of its image point?

Q3 What is the relationship between the coordinates of a point and the coordinates of its image point after a 180° rotation about the origin? If a point with coordinates (a, b) is rotated by 180° about the origin, what will the coordinates of its image point be?

A –90° rotation is equivalent to three 90° rotations. → **Q4** If you rotate an object by –90°, it will be rotated clockwise rather than counterclockwise. Suppose a point with coordinates (a, b) is rotated by –90°. What will the coordinates of the rotated point be?

Explore More

1. Using Sketchpad's Measure menu, you can measure a point's *coordinates,* a segment's *slope* and *length,* and an interior's *perimeter* and *area.* Which of these measurements are preserved (don't change) under a rotation? Which aren't?

Many people prefer to use a *polar grid* for certain kinds of graphing. To get a polar grid, choose **Polar Grid** from the Graph | Grid Form submenu (you can do this in the active sketch). Now once again measure the coordinates of a point and its image points. Then drag the points around to determine the relationship between the coordinates of rotated points.

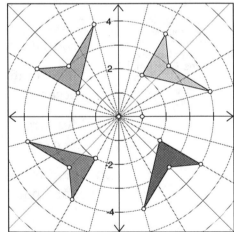

2. Plot a new point on your polar grid. Predict its polar coordinates, then check your prediction. Explain how polar coordinates are measured.

3. Rotate a point by 45° about the origin. Measure the coordinates of the original point and its image point in both a square coordinate system and a polar coordinate system. In which type of coordinate system is the relationship between the coordinates clearer?

Reflection in Geometry and Algebra

Name(s): _____

If you're like most people, you've spent at least a *little* time looking at yourself in the mirror. So you're already pretty familiar with reflection. In this activity, you'll add to your knowledge on the subject as you explore reflection from both geometric and algebraic perspectives.

Sketch and Investigate

1. In a new sketch, use the **Point** tool to draw a point.

2. With the point still selected, choose a color from the Display | Color submenu. Then choose **Trace Point** from the Display menu. Use the **Arrow** tool to drag the point around.

   The "trail" the point leaves is called its trace.

To choose the **Line** tool, press and hold the mouse button over the current **Straightedge** tool, then drag and release over the **Line** tool in the palette that appears.

3. If the trace from the previous step fades and disappears, go on to the next step. If the trace remains on the screen, choose **Preferences** from the Edit menu. On the Color panel, check the Fade Traces Over Time box and click OK.

4. Using the **Line** tool, draw a line. With the line selected, choose **Mark Mirror** from the Transform menu.

   A brief animation indicates that the mirror line has been marked.

5. Using the **Arrow** tool, select the point. Choose **Reflect** from the Transform menu.

   The point's reflected image appears.

Starting in this step, we'll refer to the two points defining the line as *line points* and the other two points as *reflecting points*.

6. Give the new point a different color and turn tracing on for it as well.

7. What will happen when you drag one of the reflecting points? Ponder this a moment. Then drag and see. What do you think will happen when you drag one of the line points? Find the answer to this question too.

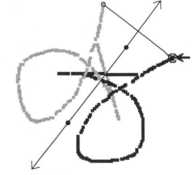

Q1 Briefly describe the two types of patterns you observed in step 7 (one when dragging a reflecting point, the other when dragging a line point).

8. Select the reflecting points; then choose **Trace Points** to toggle tracing off.

9. With the two points still selected, choose **Segment** from the Construct menu.

   A segment is constructed between the points. Drag the various objects around and observe the relationship between the line and the segment.

Q2 What angle do the line and the segment appear to make with each other? How does the line appear to divide the segment?

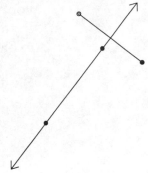

From Geometry to Algebra

Now that you've learned some geometric properties of reflection, it's time to apply this knowledge to reflection in the *x-y* plane. You'll start by exploring reflection across the *y*-axis.

10. Click in blank space to deselect all objects. Drag one of the line points so it's near the center of the sketch. With this point selected, choose **Define Origin** from the Graph menu.

    A coordinate system appears. The selected point is the origin—(0, 0).

11. Deselect all objects; then select the *y*-axis and the other line point (the one that didn't become the origin). Choose **Merge Point To Axis** from the Edit menu.

    The point "attaches" itself to the y-axis, which now acts as the mirror line.

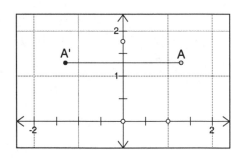

12. Select one of the reflecting points and choose **Coordinates** from the Measure menu.

    The point's (x, y) coordinate measurement appears. Drag the point and watch its coordinates change.

13. How do you think the other reflecting point's coordinates compare? Measure them to find out if you were right.

Q3 A point with coordinates (a, b) is reflected across the y-axis. What are the coordinates of its reflected image?

14. How does the distance between the two reflecting points relate to their coordinates? Make a prediction. Then select the two points and choose **Coordinate Distance** from the Measure menu. Were you right?

A special challenge is to make sure your answers to this question and Q6 work regardless of what quadrants the points are in.

Q4 A point with coordinates (a, b) is reflected across the y-axis. How far is it from its reflected image?

15. Deselect all objects. Then select the point on the y-axis that was merged in step 11. Choose **Split Point From Axis**.

The point splits from the y-axis.

16. With the point still selected, select the x-axis as well. Then choose **Merge Point To Axis** from the Edit menu.

The x-axis now acts as the mirror line. Drag one of the reflecting points and observe the various measurements.

Q5 A point with coordinates (c, d) is reflected across the x-axis. What are the coordinates of its reflected image?

Q6 A point with coordinates (c, d) is reflected across the x-axis. How far is it from its reflected image?

Explore More

1. Plot the line $y = x$. Split the point from the x-axis and merge it to the new line. What do you notice about the coordinates of the reflecting points?

2. Consider the following transformations (each is separate):

   a. Reflect a point over the x-axis, then reflect the image over the y-axis.

   b. Reflect a point over the y-axis, then reflect the image over the x-axis.

   c. Rotate a point by 180° about the origin.

   How do these three transformations compare? What would the coordinates of a point (a, b) be after each of these transformations?

Reflecting Function Plots

Name(s): _____

In the previous activity, you explored what happens when you reflect points and segments across the *x*- and *y*-axes. You learned that the *x*-coordinates of a point and its reflected image across the *y*-axis are the opposite of each other; similarly, the *y*-coordinates of a point and its reflected image across the *x*-axis are opposites. But what if you want to plot the reflection of an entire *function plot* across one of the axes?

Sketch and Investigate

To enter an x, click on the "x" in the dialog box. To take something to a power, click on the "∧" symbol in the dialog box.

→ 1. In a new sketch, use the **Plot New Function** command from the Graph menu to plot any quadratic function, such as $f(x) = x^2 - 5x + 5$.

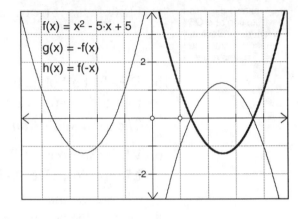

To enter f into a new function equation, click on its equation in the sketch.

→ 2. Using the **New Function** command, create the function $g(x) = -f(x)$. Then create the function $h(x) = f(-x)$.

3. The graph of one of these new functions is the reflection of the original graph across the *y*-axis; the graph of the other is the reflection across the *x*-axis. Make a conjecture as to which is which.

*To plot functions, select their equations and choose **Plot Function** from the Graph menu.*

→ 4. Plot the two new functions (first one, then the other so you know which is which). Does your conjecture seem to be correct?

5. Select the equation for $f(x)$ and its plot, then choose a color from the Display | Color submenu. With the objects still selected, choose **Thick** from the Display | Line Weight submenu. Give $g(x)$ and its plot their own color and do the same for $h(x)$ and its plot, but don't make their line weights thick.

6. Double-click the equation for $f(x)$. In the Edit Function dialog box that appears, change $f(x)$ into some other function of your choosing. Do the relationships you've been observing still hold?

Q1 Fill in the blanks:

The graphs of $y = f(x)$ and $y = -f(x)$ are reflections of each other across _____.

The graphs of $y = f(x)$ and $y = f(-x)$ are reflections of each other across _____.

Exploring Algebra with The Geometer's Sketchpad
© 2002 Key Curriculum Press

Q2 Why does it make sense, based on what you know about the reflection of points across coordinate axes, that $y = -f(x)$ reflects the plot of f across the x-axis and $y = f(-x)$ reflects it across the y-axis?

Explore More

1. In the previous activity's Explore More question 2, you learned that reflecting a point over the x–axis, then reflecting the image point over the y–axis gives the same result as if you had reflected first over the y–axis, then over the x–axis (and both were equivalent to a 180° rotation). Can you devise a function based on any $f(x)$ that, when plotted, transforms the plot of $f(x)$ in this way?

2. An *even function* is one for which $f(-x) = f(x)$. In other words, the plots of $y = f(-x)$ and $y = f(x)$ are the same. An *odd function* is one for which $f(-x) = -f(x)$. In other words, the plots of $y = f(-x)$ and $y = -f(x)$ are the same. Edit $f(x)$ in your sketch to determine which of the following functions are even, which are odd, and which are neither:

   $f(x) = x^2 + 3$ $\qquad\qquad\qquad$ $f(x) = x^3$

   $f(x) = x^3 + 3$ $\qquad\qquad\qquad$ $f(x) = x^6 + 3x^4 - 2x^2$

   $f(x) = x^5 + 3x^3 - 8x.$

3. In the previous activity's Explore More question 1, you learned that when reflecting a point across the line $y = x$, its x- and y-coordinates get switched. Here's a way of reflecting a function plot across the line $y = x$ that uses that result: Choose **Plot New Function** from the Graph menu and choose **x = f(y)** from the Equation pop-up menu. Enter $f(y)$ (by clicking first on f's equation in the sketch, then on the "y" in the dialog box) and click OK. Experiment with several different equations for $f(x)$ to see how a graph relates to its reflection across $y = x$.

Reflecting Without the Reflect Command: The Algebra of Reflection

Name(s): _____

It's easy to use Sketchpad's **Reflect** command to reflect a point across a line. But what if you didn't have Sketchpad available and you needed to know the coordinates of a reflected point? (This is actually a fairly common type of problem in computer animation.) You'll get a good algebraic workout in this activity as you find this out.

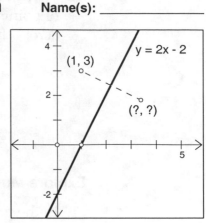

Background

In the previous activity, we observed the following about reflections:

> *When a point is reflected across a line, that line is the perpendicular bisector of the segment joining the two points.*

Here's a good low-tech way to remind yourself of what this means: Use a ruler to draw a short segment on a piece of binder paper. Fold the paper so that the two endpoints of the segment touch (you may need good light—and dark ink—to do this). The fold is the mirror line, and the two endpoints are reflections across that line. How do the fold line and the segment relate? Does the above observation now make more sense?

Sketch and Investigate

You'll start by using the observation from above to *construct* a reflected image of a point across a mirror line without using the **Reflect** command.

1. Open a new sketch. Choose **Preferences** from the Edit menu. On the Units panel, set Distance Units to **cm** (centimeters). On the Text panel, check For All New Points. Click OK.

   From now on, points will be given labels the moment they are created.

To choose the **Line** tool, press and hold the mouse button over the current **Straightedge** tool, then drag and release over the **Line** tool in the palette that appears.

2. Choose the **Line** tool and use it to draw a line. Use the **Point** tool to draw a point not on the line.

   The line is the mirror line. Your goal is to construct the mirror image of point C across this line.

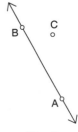

3. Using the **Arrow** tool, select point C and the line. Choose **Perpendicular Line** from the Construct menu.

   A line is constructed through the selected point, perpendicular to the selected line.

Step 2

4. Construct the point of intersection between the lines by clicking there with the **Arrow** tool.

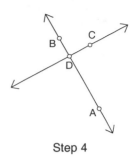

Step 4

Think about the distance and direction point *C* would have to "travel" to get to point *D*. If we could *translate* point *D* that same distance and direction, the resulting point would be at the desired location (where point *C* would be if reflected across line *AB*). A quantity that has both distance and direction is called a *vector*.

5. Deselect all objects by clicking in blank space. Select, in order, points *C* and *D*. Then choose **Mark Vector** from the Transform menu.

   A brief animation from C to D indicates that the vector has been marked.

6. Select point *D* and choose **Translate** from the Transform menu. Click Translate to translate by the marked vector. Drag point *C*.

   Do C and D' appear to be reflections of each other across line AB?

We can find the coordinates of *D'*, but how are they related to *C* and to the line of reflection *AB*? We'll need some algebra to figure this out.

An Algebraic Approach

Now the goal is to do what you just did, this time using algebra. You'll start by putting the figure into an *x-y* coordinate system. Then, you'll redo the geometric steps from above using actual equations and coordinates.

7. Drag point *A* close to the center of the sketch window and, with *A* still selected, choose **Define Origin** from the Graph menu.

   A coordinate system appears with the selected point as the origin: (0, 0).

8. Select points *B* and *C*, then choose **Coordinates** from the Measure menu.

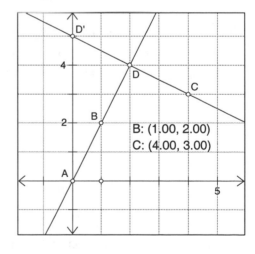

9. Choose **Snap Points** from the Graph menu. Then move *B* to (1, 2) and *C* to (4, 3).

Once you've written an answer, you can check your work by selecting the line and choosing **Equation** from the Measure menu.

→ **Q1** What is the equation of line *AB* at its current location?

Reflecting Without the Reflect Command (continued)

Remember that lines are perpendicular when the product of their slopes is –1. Also, point-slope form should be the easiest to use here.

Q2 In step 3, you constructed the line perpendicular to $\overleftrightarrow{AB}$ containing point C. Use algebra to find the equation of this line given the current locations of $\overleftrightarrow{AB}$ and point C.

Q3 In step 4, you constructed point D, the intersection of line AB and the line through C. Find the coordinates of this point by solving the system of equations made up of your answers from Q1 and Q2.

Q4 In steps 5 and 6, you translated point D by the same vector as from C to D. Using the coordinates you now have for these two points, find out what the coordinates of D' must be.

Once you've written an answer, you can check your work by moving point C in your sketch.

Q5 Redo Q2 through Q4 with point C at $(7, -1)$. In other words, use algebra to find the coordinates of the reflected image of point $(7, -1)$ across the line $y = 2x$.

Explore More

1. Redo Q2 through Q4 using (a, b) as point C. In other words, find the coordinates (in terms of a and b) of the reflected image of point (a, b) across the line $y = 2x$. How can you check to see if your answer is correct?

2. Redo Q2 through Q4 to find the coordinates of the reflected image of point (a, b) across the line $y = mx$.

Walking Rex:
An Introduction to Vectors   Name(s): _____

You know that 2 + 2 = 4. No big shock there. But what if you walk 2 miles north, turn around, then walk 2 miles south—how far have you walked? In one sense, you've walked 4 miles—that's certainly what your feet would tell you. But in another sense, you haven't really gotten anywhere. We could say: 2N + 2S = 0.

Values that have both a *magnitude* (size) and a *direction* are called **vectors**. Vectors are very useful in studying things like the flight of airplanes in wind currents and the push and pull of magnetic forces. In this activity, you'll explore some of the algebra and geometry behind vectors in the context of a walk with your faithful dog, Rex.

Walk the Dog

1. Open the sketch **Walk the Dog.gsp** from the folder **5_Transform**.

   Rex's leash is tied to a tree at the origin of an x-y coordinate system. Rex is pulling the leash tight as he excitedly waits for you to take him on a walk.

Rex has a head and tail too, of course, but those have nothing to do with the vector!

Rex's taut leash is represented by a vector—a segment with an arrowhead. The end with the arrowhead (Rex) is called the *head* and the other end (the tree) is called the *tail*. We've labeled this particular vector *j*.

Q1 One way to define vectors is by their *magnitude* (length) and *direction*. Which of these two quantities stays the same as you drag point *Rex*?

Q2 For each description of vector *j*, find Rex's coordinates.

   a. magnitude = 5; direction = 30°

   b. magnitude = 5; direction = 90°

   c. magnitude = 5; direction = 225°

Q3 A second way to define a vector is by the coordinates of its head *when its tail is at the origin.*

Use Sketchpad to find the magnitude and direction of the following vectors:

a. vector $j = (5, 0)$

b. vector $k = (3, 4)$

c. vector $l = (0, -5)$

d. vector $m = (-3, -4)$

Q4 Rex is terrified of ladybugs. Suppose a ladybug is sitting at $(5, 0)$. Where should Rex move to face the opposite direction and be as far from it as possible? What if the ladybug moves to $(3, -4)$?

Now it's time to untie the leash from the tree and take Rex for a walk.

2. Go to the second page of **Walk the Dog.gsp**: Walk 1.

   Rex is a very determined dog! As you walk him, he pulls the leash taut and always tries to steer you in the same direction (toward an interesting scent perhaps). Rex is still at the head of vector j (where the arrowhead is) and now you're at the tail.

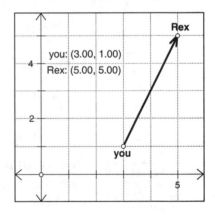

Q5 Drag vector j around the screen. Explain why, no matter where you drag it, vector j is always the same vector. Use one of the two methods for defining vectors we've discussed to support your argument.

Exploring Algebra with The Geometer's Sketchpad
© 2002 Key Curriculum Press

Q6 Suppose you stood at the point (80, 80). Where would Rex be standing? Explain how you found your answer. (Don't scroll or use Sketchpad's menus—all the information you need is on the screen.)

3. Go to the third and fourth pages of **Walk the Dog.gsp**: Walk 2 and Walk 3.

   You'll see that Rex is heading in different directions on these pages. The information presented on screen is also a little different for each page.

Q7 As in Q6, determine where Rex will be standing when you're at (80, 80) for Walk 2 and Walk 3. Explain your reasoning in each case.

Q8 Answer Q7 again, this time assuming that you have a leash twice as long and Rex heads in the same directions.

Vector Addition and Subtraction

Name(s):_____

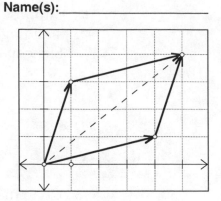

In the previous activity, you learned about vectors as you walked your dog, Rex. Now, you'll leave Rex home and go on some walks of your own. Along the way, you'll explore how vectors are added and subtracted.

Sketch and Investigate

1. Open **Walks.gsp** from the folder **5_Transform**.

The arrows over *j* and *k* indicate that they represent vectors.

You'll see two moveable vectors, $\vec{j}$ and $\vec{k}$.

You start your walk at home (the origin) heading first along a path the direction and magnitude of vector *j*, then along another path the direction and magnitude of vector *k*.

Magnitude is another word for *size* or, in this case, *length*.

Q1 Drag the vectors to find out at what coordinates you're standing when your walk is done. (Don't measure any new coordinates.) Explain how you got your answer.

Q2 Oops, we goofed—you didn't walk along $\vec{j}$, then $\vec{k}$. You walked first along $\vec{k}$, *then* $\vec{j}$. Where are you actually standing after this walk?

Your walks in Q1 and Q2 could have been more direct. Instead of following vectors *j* and *k*, you could have gone directly to the final destination along a single vector, $\vec{m}$.

Q3 Choose **vector** from the Custom Tools menu, as shown at right. This tool draws a vector with an arrow at its head. Use it to draw the vector *m* that would take you directly from home to your final destination. What are the coordinates of the head and tail of $\vec{m}$?

Exploring Algebra with The Geometer's Sketchpad
© 2002 Key Curriculum Press

As before, you won't need to measure any new coordinates.

Q4 Go to the second page of **Walks.gsp**. This time, the coordinates of only one point are given. Assuming, as before, that you start at "home," where do you end up? How did you get your answer?

Q5 Answer the same question for the walk on the third page of **Walks.gsp**. (Don't explain your answer this time.)

2. Use the **vector** tool to draw the vectors representing direct paths from "home" to your final destination in Q4 and Q5.

Vector Addition

Without knowing it, perhaps, you've been doing vector addition! In step 2 above, you found a single vector, m, that was equivalent to walking along $\vec{j}$, then $\vec{k}$. We can say that $\vec{m} = \vec{j} + \vec{k}$.

Having a coordinate system in place allowed you to find the coordinates of $\vec{m}$'s head. But if there were no coordinate grid, would you still have been able to draw $\vec{j} + \vec{k}$?

3. Go to the fourth page of **Walks.gsp**: "Adding."

4. What do you think $\vec{j} + \vec{k}$ will look like? Press the button *add j + k* to see.

5. What do you think $\vec{k} + \vec{j}$ will look like? Press *add k + j* to see.

Q6 In the space below, describe vector addition in a way that someone familiar with the basics of vectors—but not yet vector addition— would understand. Make sure to use the words *head* and *tail*.

Hint: draw
vectors *j* and *k*
so that their tails
both coincide.
When your drawing
is complete, look
for a parallelogram.

Q7 Addition of real numbers is *commutative* because $a + b = b + a$. (For example, $3 + 5 = 5 + 3 = 8$.) Is vector addition commutative? In other words, does $\vec{j} + \vec{k} = \vec{k} + \vec{j}$? Defend your answer with a drawing.

Q8 The *zero vector*, $\vec{0}$, is a vector with a magnitude of $\vec{0}$ (basically, just a point). What must be true of two vectors whose sum is $\vec{0}$?

Vector Subtraction

Before moving on to vector subtraction, consider subtraction of real numbers. Recall that by definition, $8 - 5 = 8 + (-5) = 3$. In other words, *subtracting a number is the same as adding its opposite*. The same is true with vectors: *subtracting a vector is the same as adding its opposite*.

6. Go to the fifth page of **Vectors.gsp**: "Subtracting." Experiment on this page just as you did on the previous page.

Q9 In the space below, describe vector subtraction in a way that someone familiar with the basics of vectors—but not yet vector subtraction—would understand.

Q10 Is vector subtraction commutative? In other words, does $\vec{j} - \vec{k} = \vec{k} - \vec{j}$? Defend your answer with a drawing.

Explore More

1. In the previous activity, you learned that one way of naming a vector is to use the coordinates of its head if its tail were at the origin. Assume that $\vec{j} = (j_1, j_2)$ and $\vec{k} = (k_1, k_2)$. If $\vec{j} + \vec{k} = \vec{m}$, what are the coordinates of $\vec{m}$? If $\vec{j} - \vec{k} = \vec{n}$, what are the coordinates of $\vec{n}$?

Chapter 5: Transformations and Vectors
Project Ideas

The projects below extend your knowledge of transformations and vectors and are suitable for in-class presentations, papers, or personal exploration.

1. The activities in this chapter cover three of the four basic transformations in Sketchpad's Transform menu: translation, rotation, and reflection. But the fourth, dilation, isn't covered. Explore the algebra behind dilation using a method similar to that used in the first two activities in this chapter. Experiment with negative scale factors and scale factors between 0 and 1. What is dilation? How does dilation affect the coordinates of dilated points? How does dilation affect other aspects of the sketch, such as the area and perimeter of the dilated polygon?

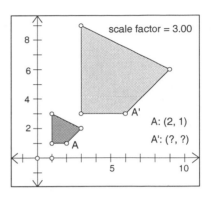

2. In the activity Rotation in the Coordinate Plane, the *polar grid* and *polar coordinates* were introduced. Explore graphing in the polar grid as follows: In a new sketch, choose **Polar Grid** from the Graph | Grid Form submenu. Choose **Plot New Function** from the Graph menu, enter 3, and click OK. Why does the resulting graph—$f(\theta) = 3$, or $r = 3$—look the way it does? Try plotting $f(\theta) = \theta$ or other functions of θ. In the New Function dialog box, choose $\theta = f(r)$ from the Equation pop-up menu. Then choose 45 to plot the function $f(r) = 45$. Explore the plots of other functions of r. In all cases, try to explain why the graph makes sense given what you know about polar coordinates.

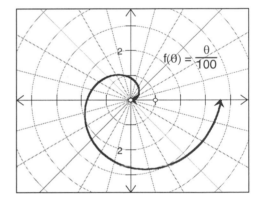

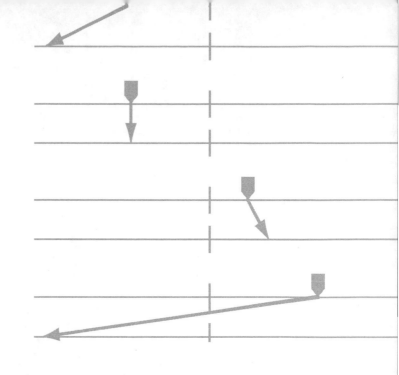

Activity Notes

Adding Integers (page 3)

Student Audience: Pre-algebra/Algebra 1

Prerequisites: None. This will be a review topic for most Algebra 1 students.

Sketchpad Proficiency: Beginner. Students manipulate a pre-made sketch.

Activity Time: 20–30 minutes

Required Sketch: Add Integers.gsp from the folder **1_Fundamentals.** Extra pages (not referred to in the activity) include a vertical version of the addition model and a version that doesn't round to integers.

General Notes: This activity works well as an introduction to integer addition for pre-algebra students, a start-of-the-year refresher for Algebra 1 students, or a supplemental activity for any student having difficulty with the topic. The most important thing is for students to actually study, understand, and use the number-line sketch. Even the strongest students make careless mistakes with integers due to relying too much on verbal rules; having an internalized picture can help. Teachers may need to encourage students who already have some experience with integers to approach this activity with a mind open to fresh perspectives.

Sketch and Investigate

Q1 –9

Q2 It's similar in that if you ignore all the negative signs, the answer is the same. For example, $3 + 9 = 12$ and $(-)3 + (-)9 = (-)12$. It's different in that the answer turns out to be negative instead of positive.

Q3 No, not possible. The reason is that you're starting to the left of the origin (because the first number is negative) and you're moving further left (because the second number is negative). You can't do this and end up to the right of the origin.

Q4 0

Q5 Each must be the opposite of the other.

Q6 –3

Q7 If the "bigger" number (longest arrow/greatest absolute value) is positive, the sum will be positive. If the "bigger" number (longest arrow/greatest absolute value) is negative, the sum will be negative.

Q8 Since the arrows go in opposite directions, in a way you are actually subtracting values. Completely ignoring negative signs for now, the answer is always the bigger addend minus the smaller addend. For example, $7 + (-5) = 2$ and $7 - 5 = 2$. Also, $-9 + 8 = -1$ and $9 - 8 = 1$.

Q9   a.   positive

  b.   negative

  c.   its opposite

  d.   positive; negative

Note that while these rules are important, memorizing them isn't necessary if students remember the number line and arrows.

Explore More

1.   a.   It makes sense because all that changes is the order in which you move one way or the other. Moving three steps to the right, then five steps to the left is the same as moving five steps to the left, then three steps to the right.

  b.   Yes, it does.

Subtracting Integers (page 6)

Student Audience: Pre-algebra/Algebra 1

Prerequisites: None. This will be a review topic for most Algebra 1 students.

Sketchpad Proficiency: Beginner. Students manipulate a pre-made sketch.

Activity Time: 25–35 minutes

Required Sketch: Subtract Integers.gsp from the folder **1_Fundamentals**. Extra pages (not referred to in the activity) include a vertical version of the subtraction model and a version that doesn't round to integers.

General Notes: This activity works well as an introduction to integer subtraction for Pre-algebra students, a start-of-the-year refresher for Algebra 1 students, or a supplemental activity for any student having difficulty with the topic. It works best if done in conjunction with the previous activity, Adding Integers, but this isn't necessary. The most important thing is for students to actually study, understand, and use the number-line sketch. Even the strongest students make careless mistakes with integers due to relying too much on verbal rules; having an internalized picture can help. Teachers may need to encourage students who already have some experience with integers to approach this activity with a mind open to fresh perspectives.

Sketch and Investigate

Q1 Ignore the green arrow for a moment: the blue arrow and the red arrow are being *added* just as in the previous activity. The red arrow represents the opposite of the green arrow. Thus, subtracting a number (the green arrow) is the same as adding its opposite (the red arrow).

Q2 –2

Q3 The number being subtracted must be bigger than the number it is subtracted from.

Q4 –9

Q5 Let's use the example from Q4, –5 – 4 = –9. Notice that 5 + 4 = 9. Thus, when subtracting a positive number from a negative number, you can just add the absolute values of the two numbers and change the sign to get your final answer.

Q6 9

Q7 –3

Q8 Let's use the example from Q6, 5 – (–4) = 9. Notice that 5 + 4 = 9. In Q7, –7 – (–4) = –3. Notice that –7 + 4 = –3. In both cases, a minus sign followed by a negative sign ("subtracting a negative") was equivalent to a plus sign ("adding a positive").

Q9 If the number being subtracted has a greater absolute value (is "more negative"), the difference will be positive. If the number being subtracted *from* has a greater absolute value, the difference will be negative.

Q10 They must be equal. Three examples:

$$5 – 5 = 0 \qquad –7 – (–7) = 0 \qquad 0 – 0 = 0$$

Explore More

1. Any pair of unequal numbers will do. For example, –4 – 7 = –11 and 7 – (–4) = 11. In all cases, the two answers will be opposites of each other.

Multiple Models of Multiplication (page 9)

Student Audience: Pre-algebra/Algebra 1

Prerequisites: None. This will be a review topic for most Algebra 1 students, though perhaps it presents things in a new way.

Sketchpad Proficiency: Beginner. Students manipulate a pre-made sketch.

Activity Time: 40–50 minutes

Required Sketch: Multiplication Models.gsp from the folder **1_Fundamentals**

General Notes: There are two main purposes behind this activity. First, the idea is to provide students with (surprise!) multiple models of multiplication—different ways of conceiving of this key operation. Students should not be allowed to do the problems in their heads without modeling them in Sketchpad—that would defeat the purpose.

The second goal of the activity is to provide various justifications for the rules for multiplying negatives. A picture is worth a thousand words, and these models may provide a more solid foundation for internalizing "a negative times a negative equals a positive" than any verbal rule.

Keep in mind that these three models of multiplication aren't the only three in this chapter. The next activity, Raz's Magic Multiplying Machine, provides a fourth model that also challenges students to broaden their thinking about multiplication, and provides compelling reasons for the rules for multiplying negatives. Either of these two activities works alone, but they work especially well together, done in either order.

Multiplication As Grouping

Q1 a. $4 \cdot 2 = 8$ b. $3 \cdot -3 = -9$

c. $1 \cdot -8 = -8$ d. $-2 \cdot 3 = -6$

e. $-1 \cdot 5 = -5$ f. $-2 \cdot -3 = 6$

g. $-8 \cdot -1 = 8$

Q2 a. $3 \cdot -4 = -12$ b. $4 \cdot -3 = -12$

These two equations are similar in that they both give the same answer, –12. In both cases, a positive number is being multiplied by a negative number. The only difference is that the number of groups and the size of each group are switched.

Q3 "Take away three groups of 4" ($-3 \cdot 4 = -12$) and "take away four groups of 3" ($-4 \cdot 3 = -12$).

Multiplication As Area

Q4 $-1 \cdot 6 = -6$; $-2 \cdot 3 = -6$; $-6 \cdot 1 = -6$; $1 \cdot -6 = -6$; $2 \cdot -3 = -6$; $3 \cdot -2 = -6$; $-6 \cdot 1 = -6$

Q5 $1 \cdot 4 = 4$; $2 \cdot 2 = 4$; $4 \cdot 1 = 4$; $-1 \cdot -4 = 4$; $-2 \cdot -2 = 4$; $-4 \cdot -1 = 4$

Q6 Every square number can be modeled with a square in the area multiplication model. For example, 4 can be modeled by $2 \cdot 2$ or $-2 \cdot -2$, both of which are squares.

(While it's true that –4 can also be modeled with squares, $2 \cdot -2$ or $-2 \cdot 2$, these don't count since the base and height don't equal each other. This can be seen as a weakness of this model, or perhaps as an opportunity for a sneak preview at imaginary numbers.)

Multiplication As Scaling

Q7 a. The mapping segments point straight down, parallel to each other. Every number maps to itself. For example, $2 \cdot 1 = 2$, $-3 \cdot 1 = -3$, $0 \cdot 1 = 0$, etc.

b. The mapping segments point in toward the origin. Every number maps to a number whose absolute value is less than its own absolute value (or equal to, in the case of 0), but whose sign is the same. For a scale factor of 0.5, for example, $2 \cdot 0.5 = 1$, $-3 \cdot 0.5 = -1.5$, $0 \cdot 0.5 = 0$, etc.

c. The mapping segments cross the origin. Every number maps to a number with the opposite sign (except for 0, which points, as always, to itself). For a scale factor of –2, for example, $2 \cdot -2 = -4$, $-3 \cdot -2 = 6$, $0 \cdot 0 = 0$, etc.

Q8 a. $A = 0.25$ b. $A = -2$

c. $A = -1$ d. $A = -0.1$

Q9 In each pair, the numbers are reciprocals of each other. For example, in part a, $B = 4/1$ and $A = 1/4$.

Multiple Models of Multiplication

Continued from previous page.

"Summing" Up

Q10 Many possible answers. We feel that Grouping is particularly effective as an introduction to multiplication. It corresponds with most people's basic conception of multiplication, so it's a good place to start. Area is particularly effective at showing the "dimensionality" of multiplication—how multiplying two one-dimensional objects produces a two-dimensional object. Scaling is good for showing how multiplication affects an entire set of objects. It also, by the way, serves as a great introduction to dynagraphs in chapter 4!

Q11 Both Grouping (especially when using the terms "put together" and "take away") and Scaling are effective at demonstrating the rules of multiplication for negatives. Area is less effective for this, in our view, because there is no compelling reason why the rectangles in the first and third quadrants are blue and those in the second and fourth quadrants are red.

Explore More

1. Pairs of equations, such as $2 \cdot -5 = -10$ and $-5 \cdot 2 = -10$, should be modeled. We find Area especially useful for demonstrating commutativity because it's so easy to see that the two rectangles have the same area and sign.

Raz's Magic Multiplying Machine (page 12)

Student Audience: Pre-algebra/Algebra 1

Prerequisites: None. This will be a review topic for most Algebra 1 students.

Sketchpad Proficiency: Beginner. Students manipulate a pre-made sketch.

Activity Time: 30–40 minutes

Required Sketches: Multiplying Machine.gsp, Mystery Machines.gsp, and **Mystery Combos.gsp** from the folder **1_Fundamentals**

General Notes: This is a useful activity, not only for reviewing multiplication of positive and negative numbers, but also for developing number sense in general. Many important number properties, such as multiplication of negatives, square roots, ratios and proportions, and multiplication by numbers between 0 and 1 (and also between –1 and 0), can be demonstrated and explored using these simple "machines." The key is to not only to observe behavior, but also to explain the behavior mathematically. "What is it about multiplication that makes the machine behave like this?" Students should be encouraged to do their own explorations and observe their own patterns.

Note that this isn't the only activity in this chapter covering multiplication. The previous activity, Multiple Models of Multiplication, covers three separate models of multiplication, each with its own particular emphasis and each with its own justification of the rules for multiplying negatives. And the next activity, Exploring the Properties of the Four Arithmetic Operations, does just what the title suggests with Raz-like machines built for each of the four fundamental operations.

Sketch and Investigate

Q1 $0.5 \cdot 6 = 3$.

Q2 Many possible answers.

Students might be asked what different *types* of answers to this question are possible. (One possibility is that both factors could be positive integers. Another is that one could be a positive integer and the other could be a decimal between 0 and 1.)

Q3 The only two possible locations are at 0 $(0 \cdot 0 = 0)$ and 1 $(1 \cdot 1 = 1)$.

To show that these are the only two solutions, solve the equation $x \cdot x = x$.

Q4 *A* must be at –1.

Q5 No, this isn't possible. When A and B are to the left of 0, $A \cdot B$ is to its right, since a negative times a negative equals a positive. When $A \cdot B$ is to the left of 0, one of the factors is also to the left of 0 and the other is to the right, since a negative times a positive is a negative.

Q6 Many possible answers. In all cases, both A and B are between 0 and 1.

Q7 B and $A \cdot B$ stay right on top of each other. This makes sense because any number times 1 equals itself.

Q8 B and $A \cdot B$ move in opposite directions and at the same speed. They can be thought of as reflections of each other across 0. This makes sense because any number times –1 equals its opposite—the number just as "big" but on the other side of 0.

Q9 B moves faster than $A \cdot B$—twice as fast, to be exact. This is because a number times a number between 0 and 1 gives a result smaller (closer to 0) than the original number.

Q10 The two possible answers are 2 and –2.

Q11 As you drag A to the left, $A \cdot B$ moves to the left as well. As A approaches 0, $A \cdot B$ approaches 0 too, and when $A = 0$, $A \cdot B = 0$. It makes sense that as you keep dragging A to the left, $A \cdot B$ would continue its previous behavior, namely moving to the left as well, into negative territory.

Q12 With B to the left of 0, A and $A \cdot B$ move in opposite directions. As you drag A to the left, $A \cdot B$ moves to the right. As A approaches 0, $A \cdot B$ approaches 0 too, but from the other side, and when $A = 0$, $A \cdot B = 0$. It makes sense that as you keep dragging A to the left, $A \cdot B$ would continue its previous behavior, namely moving to the right, back into positive territory.

Explore More

1. To find 0, drag A (or B) until it and $A \cdot B$ are right on top of each other. This spot is 0. This method works because any number times 0 equals 0. Thus, when A is 0, $A \cdot B$ will also be 0. Once you've positioned A, you can check your work by dragging B. If A is at zero, then A and $A \cdot B$ will remain on top of each other as B is dragged.

    To find 1, drag A until B and $A \cdot B$ are right on top of each other (or drag B until A and $A \cdot B$ are right on top of each other). A is at 1. This method works because any number times 1 equals itself. Thus, when A is 1, B and $A \cdot B$ will equal each other. Again, check your work by dragging. If A is at one, then B and $A \cdot B$ will remain on top of each other as B is dragged.

2. Move A and B so that they're both at 1/2. $(1/2)(1/2) = 1/4$, so $A \cdot B$ is at 1/4. Mark this spot using the **Point** tool. Now move either A or B to 1/4 (where you just marked). $A \cdot B$ will now be at 1/8 because $(1/2)(1/4) = 1/8$.

3. To find 0, drag A until B and $A + B$ are right on top of each other (or drag B until A and $A + B$ are right on top of each other). This works because any number plus 0 equals itself. Thus, when A is 0, B and $A + B$ will equal each other. (Note that the method for finding 0 on an "adding machine" is the same as that for finding 1 on a "multiplying machine." This is because 1 is the *identity element* for multiplication and 0 is the *identity element* for addition.)

    It's impossible to find 1.

4. Mystery combo 1: $C = A + 2B$

    Mystery combo 2: $C = A - B$

    Mystery combo 3: $C = AB - 1$

Exploring the Properties of the Four Arithmetic Operations (page 16)

Student Audience: Pre-algebra/Algebra 1

Prerequisites: None, though it may help to have done the previous activity, Raz's Magic Multiplying Machine, prior to this one.

Sketchpad Proficiency: Beginner. Students manipulate a pre-made sketch.

Activity Time: Varies widely, depending on the approach (see General Notes). It would take most students, working alone, much longer than one class period to fill in charts for all nine descriptions. By working in groups, with each group responsible for different descriptions, activity time can be reduced to one, or perhaps two, class periods.

Required Sketch: Arithmetic Machines.gsp from the folder **1_Fundamentals**

General Notes: This activity challenges students to analyze and understand the four fundamental arithmetic operations—addition, subtraction, multiplication, and division—from a visual perspective.

It's possible to answer any of the questions in this activity without using the arithmetic machines at all. But that defeats its purpose: Watching the machines in action as you drag pointers A and B can be fascinating. The four arithmetic operations, normally computed on a discrete, case-by-case basis, yield new insights when viewed from a continuous, motion-based perspective.

To get the most out of this activity, it's necessary that students not treat the process of finding the answers as a purely mechanical one, dragging the pointers around without thinking about the meaning behind the various arrangements. For this reason, it's probably best not to assign too many questions at one time. Dividing the class into groups will make the work more manageable and allow time for reflection.

One possible variation to the approach suggested in the activity is to focus on one operation for several descriptions at a time. For example, students might focus on addition and fill out the four cells of the chart for D1–D4. On a new chart, they might then focus on subtraction for those same four descriptions. For less experienced students, this may prove to be a more coherent approach as they aren't asked to switch from one operation to the next as often.

You may find that your students have difficulty generalizing their results as requested in part c of the Arithmetic Operations Chart. Nonetheless, they can use the patterns they observe while dragging pointers A and B to make their findings as general as possible.

The questions in this activity are really just the tip of the iceberg when it comes to exploring the arithmetic machines. Why not challenge your students to write and share some of their own questions? Here are a few to consider:

- Describe the behavior of $A \div B$ as B is dragged back and forth through 0.

- If $A \cdot B$ equals 0, does knowing the value of A allow you to determine a unique value for B?

- If $A \div B$ equals 0, does knowing the value of A allow you to determine a unique value for B?

- When is $A - B$ greater (or less) than $A + B$?

- When is $A \cdot B$ greater (or less) than $A \div B$?

- Under what circumstances does $A + B = A - B$ regardless of where you drag A?

- Under what circumstances does $A \cdot B = A \div B$ regardless of where you drag A?

Sketch and Investigate

D1 Addition:
  a. $A + B = 0$
  b. Yes. Answers will vary.
  c. Whenever both numbers are the opposite of each other (or both equal 0), their sum is 0.

  Subtraction:
  a. $A - B = 0$
  b. Yes. Answers will vary.
  c. Whenever two numbers equal each other, their difference is 0.

  Multiplication:
  a. $A \cdot B = 0$
  b. Yes. Answers will vary.
  c. In order for the product of two numbers to be 0, at least one factor must equal 0.

  Division:
  a. $A \div B = 0$
  b. Yes. Answers will vary.
  c. In order for the quotient of two numbers to be 0, the numerator must be 0 and the denominator must be anything but 0.

D2 Addition:

a. $A + B = 1$

b. Yes. Answers will vary.

c. In order for the sum of two numbers to be 1, their average must be 0.5.

Subtraction:

a. $A - B = 1$

b. Yes. Answers will vary.

c. If the difference of two numbers is 1, the first number must be one greater than the second number.

Multiplication:

a. $A \cdot B = 1$

b. Yes. Answers will vary.

c. In order for the product of two numbers to be 1, the numbers must be reciprocals.

Division:

a. $A \div B = 1$

b. Yes. Answers will vary.

c. In order for the quotient of two numbers to be 1, the numbers must be non-zero and equal one another.

D3 Addition:

a. A, B, and $A + B$ all sit at the same point.

b. Yes, though only one possibility.

c. In order for two numbers and their sum to equal each other, they must all equal 0.

Subtraction:

a. A, B, and $A - B$ all sit at the same point.

b. Yes, though only one possibility.

c. In order for two numbers and their difference to equal each other, they must all be 0.

Multiplication:

a. A, B, and $A \cdot B$ all sit at the same point.

b. Yes, though only two possibilities.

c. In order for two numbers and their product to all equal each other, the numbers must all be 0 or all be 1.

Division:

a. A, B, and $A \div B$ all sit at the same point.

b. Yes, though only one possibility.

c. In order for two numbers and their product to all equal each other, the numbers must all be 1.

D4 Addition:

a. A and $A + B$ move in unison, always sitting together, no matter where you drag A.

b. Yes, though only one possibility.

c. In order for A and $A + B$ to move together, B must equal 0.

Subtraction:

a. A and $A - B$ move in unison, always sitting together, no matter where you drag A.

b. Yes, though only one possibility.

c. In order for A and $A - B$ to move together, B must equal 0.

Multiplication:

a. A and $A \cdot B$ move in unison, always sitting together, no matter where you drag A.

b. Yes, though only one possibility.

c. In order for A and $A \cdot B$ to move together, B must equal 1.

Division:

a. A and $A \div B$ move in unison, always sitting together, no matter where you drag A.

b. Yes, though only one possibility.

c. In order for A and $A \div B$ to move together, B must equal 1.

D5 Addition:

a. A, B, and $A + B$ are all to the right of 0.

b. Yes. Answers will vary.

c. Whenever A and B are to the right of 0, so is their sum.

Subtraction:

a. A, B, and $A - B$ are all to the right of 0.

b. Yes. Answers will vary.

c. If A and B are to the right of 0, and A is greater than B, then $A - B$ will be to the right of 0.

Multiplication:

a. A, B, and $A \cdot B$ are all to the right of 0.

b. Yes. Answers will vary.

c. Whenever A and B are to the right of 0, so is $A \cdot B$.

Division:

a. A, B, and $A \div B$ are all to the right of 0.

b. Yes. Answers will vary.

c. Whenever A and B are to the right of 0, so is $A \div B$.

Exploring the Properties of the Four Arithmetic Operations

Continued from previous page.

D6 Addition:
  a. A, B, and $A + B$ are all to the left of 0.
  b.   Yes. Answers will vary.
  c.   Whenever A and B are to the left of 0, so is $A + B$.

Subtraction:
  a. A, B, and $A - B$ are all to the left of 0.
  b.   Yes. Answers will vary.
  c.   If A and B are to the left of 0, and A is less than B, then $A - B$ will be to the left of 0.

Multiplication:
  a. A, B, and $A \cdot B$ are all to the left of 0.
  b.   No, it is not possible.

Division:
  a. A, B, and $A \div B$ are all to the left of 0.
  b.   No, it is not possible.

D7 Addition:
  a. $A + B$ is to the right of both A and B.
  b.   Yes. Answers will vary.
  c. $A + B$ is greater than both A and B whenever A and B are both greater than 0.

Subtraction:
  a. $A - B$ is to the right of both A and B.
  b.   Yes. Answers will vary.
  c. $A - B$ is greater than both A and B whenever B is less than 0 and A is greater than $2B$.

Multiplication:
  a. $A \cdot B$ is to the right of both A and B.
  b.   Yes. Answers will vary.
  c. $A \cdot B$ is greater than both A and B whenever A and B are both negative, or whenever A and B are both greater than 1.

Division:
  a. $A \div B$ is to the right of both A and B.
  b.   Yes. Answers will vary.
  c. $A \div B$ is greater than both A and B whenever A and B are both negative. The statement is also true whenever B is between 0 and 1 and A is greater than B^2.

D8 Addition:
  a. $A + B$ is between A and B.
  b.   Yes. Answers will vary.
  c. $A + B$ is between A and B whenever A is less than 0 and B is greater than 0.

Subtraction:
  a. $A - B$ is between A and B.
  b.   Yes. Answers will vary.
  c. $A - B$ is between A and B whenever B is less than 0 and A is less than $2B$.

Multiplication:
  a. $A \cdot B$ is between A and B.
  b.   Yes. Answers will vary.
  c. $A \cdot B$ is between A and B whenever A is between 0 and 1 and B is greater than 1. The relationship also holds whenever A is negative and B is between 0 and 1.

Division:
  a. $A \div B$ is between A and B.
  b.   Yes. Answers will vary.
  c. $A \div B$ is between A and B whenever be 1, the numbers must be non-zero and equal one another.

D9 Addition:
  a. $A + B$ is to the left of both A and B.
  b.   Yes. Answers will vary.
  c. $A + B$ is less than both A and B whenever A and B are both less than 0.

Subtraction:
  a. $A - B$ is to the left of both A and B.
  b.   Yes. Answers will vary.
  c. $A - B$ is less than both A and B whenever B is greater than 0 and A is less than $2B$.

Multiplication:
  a. $A \cdot B$ is to the left of both A and B.
  b.   Yes. Answers will vary.
  c. $A \cdot B$ is less than both A and B whenever A and B lie between 0 and 1. The relationship also holds whenever A is less than 0 and B is greater than 1.

Division:
  a. $A \div B$ is to the left of both A and B.
  b.   Yes. Answers will vary.
  c. $A \div B$ is less than both A and B whenever B is between 0 and 1 and A is between 0 and B^2. The relationship also holds whenever A is less than 0 and B is greater than 1.

Exploring Algebra with The Geometer's Sketchpad
© 2002 Key Curriculum Press

Introducing the Coordinate Plane (page 18)

Student Audience: Pre-algebra/Algebra 1

Prerequisites: None. This will be a review topic for most Algebra 1 students.

Sketchpad Proficiency: Beginner

Activity Time: 25–35 minutes

Example Sketch: Coordinate Plane.gsp from the folder **1_Fundamentals.** The first page shows the coordinate system as it would be after step 6. The second page shows the coordinate system as it would be after step 9. The last page, "The coordinate plane," shows a coordinate system with the axes, quadrants, and control points labeled. This page is designed for use in a demonstration.

General Notes: This activity works well as an introduction to the coordinate plane for Pre-algebra students, a start-of-the-year refresher for Algebra 1 students, or a supplemental activity for any student having difficulty with the topic.

Sketch and Investigate

Q1 The *x*-coordinate measures the number of units the point is to the right or left of the *y*-axis. A positive *x*-coordinate means the point is to the right of the *y*-axis and a negative *x*-coordinate means it's to the left.

The *y*-coordinate measures the number of units the point is above or below the *x*-axis. A positive *y*-coordinate means the point is above the *x*-axis and a negative *y*-coordinate means it's below.

Q2 The upper-right quadrant is quadrant I. The upper-left quadrant is quadrant II. The lower-left quadrant is quadrant III. The lower-right quadrant is quadrant IV.

Thus, the quadrants increase as you go counterclockwise starting from the upper-right quadrant.

Q3 In each case, the answer shown depicts *all* possible answers with integer coordinates on the grid provided. The question asks for four answers, so any four of the points shown is a correct response.

a.
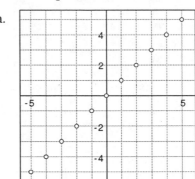

b.
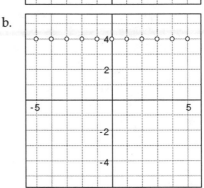

c.
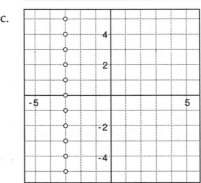

Q4 If the *x*-coordinate of a point is 0, it lies somewhere on the *y*-axis.

Q5 If the *y*-coordinate of a point is 0, it lies somewhere on the *x*-axis.

Introducing the Coordinate Plane

Continued from previous page.

Q6 Many possible answers for each. Only four possible pairs are shown for each problem.

a. Any pair of points whose coordinates are reversed in this way will be reflections of each other across the line $y = x$ (shown dashed).

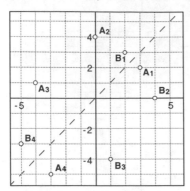

b. Any pair of points satisfying the given conditions will be reflections of each other across the x-axis.

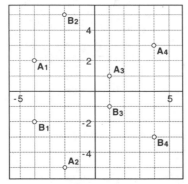

c. Any pair of points satisfying the given conditions will be reflections of each other across the y-axis.

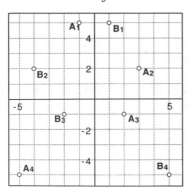

Equivalent Expressions: The Border Problem (page 22)

Student Audience: Algebra 1

Prerequisites: Students need to know how to find the areas of squares and rectangles and have some basic facility with algebraic notation.

Sketchpad Proficiency: Intermediate. Students construct interiors and make calculations using a measurement in the sketch.

Activity Time: 20–30 minutes

Required Sketch: **Border.gsp** from the folder **1_Fundamentals**

General Notes: The concept of units isn't explored explicitly in this activity. If *s* is the side length of the square—and is therefore measured in linear units such as centimeters (cm)—how can *s* also represent the area of one of the green rectangles, which should use square units such as cm²? The answer is that the area of the green rectangle is the product of its lengths, or $(s \text{ cm}) \cdot (1 \text{ cm}) = s \text{ cm}^2$ (assuming we're in centimeters). This is a good topic for class discussion.

This activity also works well as an all-class activity where there's just one computer in the classroom (with projection, hopefully). In fact, this was how this activity was initially designed and used. Here's the basic idea (many modifications are, of course, possible): Describe the situation to the class and have students make the appropriate drawing. Then ask the class for an expression for the border area. Have whoever came up with the expression justify it with a drawing. Then open up **Border.gsp** and show them this solution in Sketchpad. Calculate the area expression and ask if it seems to give the right answer for various values of *s*. Then have students come up with several more expressions on their own or in groups. One by one have students (or possibly group representatives) build their expressions in Sketchpad and do the associated calculations. Finish up the activity with a discussion of the various expressions—why some worked and why some didn't.

Sketch and Investigate

Q1 The variable s is the area of one of the green rectangles (as explained in the first paragraph of General Notes). The area of all four of these is then $4s$. The area of one of the yellow squares is 1 since they are 1 by 1 squares. The area of all four squares is then 4 and the total area of the border is $4s + 4$.

Q2 $4(s + 1)$

The area of any one of the four rectangles is $s + 1$ since each extends one unit beyond the side length s. (In other words, each is a green rectangle plus a yellow square.) The area of all four rectangles is then $4(s + 1)$.

Q3 Many possible answers. Here are several:

$2(s + 2) + 2s$

$s + s + s + s + 1 + 1 + 1 + 1$

$(s + 2) + 3s + 2$

$(s + 2) + 2(s + 1) + s$

$3(s + 1) + s + 1$

Explore More

1. See Q3.

2. The plots should all be right on top of each other.

3. One way to approach this would be to show that all of the expression are equivalent to $4s + 4$. By the transitive property, they are all then equivalent to each other. To prove that $4(s + 1)$ is equivalent to $4s + 4$, for example, simply invoke the distributive property.

The Distributive Property: Diving In (page 24)

Student Audience: Algebra 1

Prerequisites: Students need to know how to find the areas of rectangles and have some basic facility with algebraic notation.

Sketchpad Proficiency: Intermediate. Students make calculations based on measured values and use custom tools.

Activity Time: 25–35 minutes

Required Sketch: Diving In.gsp from the folder **1_Fundamentals**

General Notes: This is the first of three activities using virtual Sketchpad algebra tiles. Any of the three activities can be done on its own, though they work best if all three are done in the order they appear in the book.

It's important that students drag the sliders for x and y periodically—this is the big advantage of using Sketchpad algebra tiles, after all. First, dragging tests whether or not they've used the custom tools properly. But more important, it reinforces the fact that x and y are *variables* and that the relationships discovered work no matter what their values. At some point, students may wish to make x or y equal 1 cm (the length of 1 unit) or a multiple thereof. They can then check the relationship for this particular simple value of the variable.

Construction Tips

Step 3 or 4: As an example of how to use the Calculator, here's the sequence of clicks and keystrokes for entering $a(b + c)$:

In the New Calculation dialog box,

- click a's measurement in the sketch
- type a '*' from the keyboard or click it in the dialog box
- type or click a '('
- click on $(b + c)$'s measurement in the sketch
- type or click a ')'
- click OK

The keystroke sequence for $a \cdot b + a \cdot c$ is similar.

Q3 through Q5: When using the custom tools to create tiles, it's very important to always click on an existing point in the sketch (as opposed to clicking in blank space or on some other type of object). The point you wish to click on will highlight when the

The Distributive Property: Diving In

Continued from previous page.

tool is positioned properly; when you see the point highlighted, it's time to click. If you goof up, just choose **Undo** from the Edit menu. Improperly constructed tiles will be especially apparent when adjusting the sliders.

Sketch and Investigate

Q1 $a(b + c) = a \cdot b + a \cdot c$

Q2 The 3 in the factored expression $3(x + 2)$ is represented by the three yellow unit squares on the outside left of the corner piece. The $(x + 2)$ is represented by the blue x and three unit pieces along the top of the corner piece.

The expanded form $3x + 6$ is represented by the three blue x tiles and six yellow unit tiles inside the corner piece.

Q3 $4(x + 1)$

Q4 $y^2 + 3y$

Q5 a. $6x + 3$ b. $3x^2 + 6x$
    c. $2y^2 + 5y$ d. $2(y + 4)$
    e. $x(x + 7)$ f. $3y(y + 1)$

Q6 The other factored form for f. in Q5 is $y(3y + 3)$. This isn't fully factored because a 3 can still be factored out of the second factor. In other words, $3y + 3 = 3(y + 1)$. In general, the more "compact" and "square" you can make the inner rectangle, the more factored an expression it represents.

Note that $3y^2 + 3y$ can also be factored as $3(y^2 + y)$, but this can't be represented in this model because the second factor isn't *linear* (it has a quadratic, or squared, term).

Explore More

2. Yes, the distributive property does apply. There are several ways to change the model to allow the use of negatives. Tiles the same size and shape as the other tiles, but of different color, could be used for negatives. In fact, a variation of this strategy is used in the sketch **Advanced Algebra Tiles.gsp** that came with the program (located in the folder **Sketchpad | Samples | Sketches | Algebra**). With actual physical algebra tiles, tiles are often "stacked" to represent subtraction, negative numbers, or the opposite of a variable. Read a book on algebra tiles to learn more.

Expanding the Product of Two Binomials (page 27)

Student Audience: Algebra 1

Prerequisites: Students need to know how to find the areas of rectangles and have some basic facility with algebraic notation.

Sketchpad Proficiency: Intermediate. Students make calculations based on measured values and use custom tools.

Activity Time: 20–30 minutes

Required Sketch: Binomials.gsp from the folder **1_Fundamentals**

General Note: This activity and the next—Factoring Trinomials—are designed as companion activities. Either can be done alone, but when done together (not necessarily on the same day), they complement and reinforce each other nicely. Furthermore, these activities work especially well if done sometime after the previous activity, Diving In. Since the math is a little simpler in Diving In, it may serve as a gentler introduction to the algebra tiles.

As mentioned in the previous activity, it's important that students drag the sliders for x and y periodically—this is the big advantage of using Sketchpad algebra tiles, after all. First, dragging tests whether or not they've used the custom tools properly. But more important, it reinforces the fact that x and y are *variables* and that the relationships discovered work no matter what their values. At some point, students may wish to make x or y equal 1 cm (the length of 1 unit) or a multiple thereof. They can then check the relationship for this particular simple value of the variable.

Construction Tips

Steps 2, 6, 7, and Q3: When using the custom tools to create tiles, it is very important to always click on an existing point in the sketch (as opposed to clicking in blank space or on some other type of object). The point you wish to click on will highlight when the tool is positioned properly; when you see the point highlighted, it's time to click. If you goof up, just choose **Undo** from the Edit menu. Improperly constructed tiles will be especially apparent when adjusting the sliders.

Step 3: As an example of how to use the Calculator, here's the sequence of clicks and keystrokes for evaluating $x^2 + 8x + 15$:

In the New Calculation dialog box,

- click x's measurement in the sketch
- type a '^' (shift+6) from the keyboard or click it in the dialog box
- type or click a '+' followed by an '8'
- click x's measurement in the sketch (notice that you don't need a multiplication symbol here)
- type or click a '+' followed by '15'
- click OK

The keystroke sequence for $(x + 3)(x + 5)$ is similar.

Sketch and Investigate

Q1 The term x^2 refers to the big square in the upper left of the rectangle you built inside the corner piece. It's the product of the x from $(x + 3)$ and the x from $(x + 5)$.

The term $8x$ refers to all of the rectangular tiles in the rectangle inside the corner piece—$5x$ from the upper right and $3x$ from the lower left. $5x$ is the product of the x from $(x + 3)$ and the 5 from $(x + 5)$. $3x$ is the product of the x from $(x + 5)$ and the 3 from $(x + 3)$.

The number 15 refers to the 15 yellow squares at the bottom right of the rectangle. It's the product of the 3 from $(x + 3)$ and the 5 from $(x + 5)$.

Q2 $y^2 + 5y + 4$

Q3 a. $x^2 + 5x + 6$
   b. $2y^2 + 7y + 3$
   c. $x^2 + xy + 2x + 2y$
   d. $x^2 + 4x + 4$
   e. $2x^2 + 5xy + 2y^2$
   f. $6y^2 + 8y + 2$

Explore More

1. See Explore More 2 from the previous activity.

Factoring Trinomials (page 29)

Student Audience: Algebra 1

Prerequisites: Students need to know how to find the areas of rectangles and have some basic facility with algebraic notation. The activity is most effective if students have previous experience expanding binomials, possibly by doing the previous activity.

Sketchpad Proficiency: Intermediate. Students make calculations based on measured values and use custom tools.

Activity Time: 20–30 minutes

Required Sketch: Trinomials.gsp from the folder 1_Fundamentals

General Note: This activity and the previous one— Expanding the Product of Two Binomials—are designed as companion activities. Either can be done alone, but when done together (not necessarily on the same day), they complement and reinforce each other nicely. Furthermore, these activities work especially well if done sometime after the activity Diving In. Since the math is a little simpler in Diving In, it may serve as a gentler introduction to the algebra tiles.

As mentioned in the previous activities, it's important that students drag the sliders for x and y periodically—this is the big advantage of using Sketchpad algebra tiles, after all. First, dragging tests whether or not they've used the custom tools properly. But more important, it reinforces the fact that x and y are *variables* and that the relationships discovered work no matter what their values. At some point, students may wish to make x or y equal 1 cm (the length of 1 unit) or a multiple thereof. They can then check the relationship for this particular simple value of the variable.

Construction Tips

Step 2: If students haven't done either of the previous two activities, this step may be confusing. "Building the length and width of the rectangle" means placing tiles along the left and top sides of the rectangle on the other sides of the solid rays ("outside the corner piece"). Only tiles with a unit width can go along these borders, so only x tiles (x by 1 units), y tiles (y by 1 units), and unit ("1") tiles will fit.

Steps 2, 5, and Q1–Q3: When using the custom tools to create tiles, it is very important to always click on an existing point in the sketch (as opposed to clicking in blank space or on some other type of

Factoring Trinomials

Continued from previous page.

object). The point you wish to click on will highlight when the tool is positioned properly; when you see the point highlighted, it's time to click. If you goof up, just choose **Undo** from the Edit menu. Improperly constructed tiles will be especially apparent when adjusting the sliders.

Step 3: As an example of how to use the Calculator, here's the sequence of clicks and keystrokes for evaluating $x^2 + 3x + 2$:

In the New Calculation dialog box,

- click x's measurement in the sketch
- type a '^' (shift+6) from the keyboard or click it in the dialog box
- type or click a '+' followed by a '3'
- click x's measurement in the sketch (notice that you don't need a multiplication symbol here)
- type or click a '+' followed by a '2'
- click OK

The keystroke sequence for $(x + 1)(x + 2)$ is similar.

Sketch and Investigate

Q1 $(x + 3)(x + 2)$

Q2 a. $(x + 6)(x + 1)$ b. $(y + 4)(y + 2)$
  c. $(y + 6)(y + 2)$ d. $(x + 2y)(x + 2y)$
  e. $(2x + 1)(x + 1)$ f. $(4y + 3)(y + 1)$

In all cases, the two factors can be reversed.

Q3 There's no way to make a perfect rectangle with this group of tiles. The x's can all be lined up along one of x^2's sides, or three along one side and one along the other, or two along either side. These are the only three possibilities and in none of these cases do the six unit squares fit in.

Q4 The second term is the sum and the third term is the product of the same two numbers. Take, for example, $x^2 + 6x + 8$. 6 is the sum of 4 and 2, and 8 is the product of 4 and 2. Thus, this trinomial factors to $(x + 4)(x + 2)$.

Explore More

1. The only expressions that can be represented by more than one differently shaped rectangle are those with a constant factor common to each term. There are no such expressions in this activity. An example is $2x^2 + 12x + 16$. Notice that 2 is a common factor of each term. This expression can be factored and represented with algebra tiles either as $(2x + 8)(x + 2)$ or $(2x + 4)(x + 4)$. Neither of these, of course, is fully factored, which would be $2(x + 4)(x + 2)$.

Squares and Square Roots (page 31)

Student Audience: Algebra 1

Prerequisites: None. Some familiarity with rational numbers, irrational numbers, and the Pythagorean Theorem helps.

Sketchpad Proficiency: Beginner

Activity Time: 20-30 minutes

Required Sketch: Squares.gsp from the folder 1_Fundamentals

General Note: An important concept that's touched on in the activity (and in Project 1 at the end of the chapter) but not covered in much depth is rational versus irrational numbers. Teachers may want to start the activity by giving students a little background on this topic. Interesting questions to ask (once the definitions are understood) are: "Could the square of an irrational number be a rational number," "Could the square root of an irrational number be a rational number," and "Could a square have an irrational side length but a rational area?"

Sketch and Investigate

Q1 The area of a square is the *square* of its side length.

The side length of a square is the *square root* of its area.

(This is why taking something to the second power is called "squaring" and why "square root" is called what it is.)

Q2 The formula for area of a square is $A = s \cdot s$ (where s refers to the length of a side). Multiplying something by itself *is* squaring; thus, area is the square of side length. Similarly, finding out what number times itself gives a certain result is "square rooting"; thus, side length is the square root of area.

Q3 There are *exactly* 12 whole numbers whose areas can be represented on a geoboard, 13 if you include 0. The completed table should contain 12 of the 13 entries listed here.

n	0	1	2	4	5
$\sqrt{n}$	0	1	1.41	2	2.24
n	8	9	10	13	16
$\sqrt{n}$	2.28	3	3.16	3.61	4
n	17	18	20		
$\sqrt{n}$	4.12	4.24	4.47		

Q4 It's impossible to find the square root of every whole number using squares drawn on a rectangular grid. For example, it's impossible to draw a square with area 7 square units on a grid. The simplest way to see this is trial and error: just drag one vertex point to all of the points within a certain region and you'll see that certain results aren't possible.

Q5 The first eight numbers in the sequence are:

2, 8, 18, 32, 50, 72, 98, 128

Divide each term by 2 to see that this sequence is double the sequence of perfect squares.

Q6 Some possible answers, and the Pythagorean triples they came from, are listed below.

5	(3, 4, 5)	17	(8, 15, 17)
10	(6, 8, 10)	20	(12, 16, 20)
13	(5, 12, 13)	25	(15, 20, 25)
15	(9, 12, 15)	25	(7, 24, 25)

The last two answers are only possible in an enlarged sketch window.

Where does Pythagoras fit in? Draw a horizontal line through the bottom point of the slanted square and a vertical line through the rightmost point. The triangle formed is a right triangle whose hypotenuse is a side of the square. The legs are always whole numbers; the hypotenuse/square side is a whole number when the three sides form a Pythagorean triple.

Explore More

1. Draw an "unslanted" square around a slanted square as shown in the diagram. The larger square has a whole number area since its side length is a whole number. The four triangles formed are congruent. Put them together in pairs to form two rectangles, each of which has a whole number area since all lengths and widths are whole numbers. The area of the inside square equals the area of the outside square minus the combined areas of the four triangles. A (larger) whole number minus a (smaller) whole number is a whole number.

Points "Lining Up" in the Plane (page 37)

Student Audience: Pre-algebra/Algebra 1

Prerequisites: Familiarity with the Cartesian plane. The term *absolute value* is used and briefly defined, but it isn't a major focus of the activity.

Sketchpad Proficiency: Beginner. Students construct points and measure their coordinates.

Activity Time: 20–30 minutes

Required Sketch: Line Up.gsp from the folder 2_Lines

General Notes: The purpose of this activity is to give students an informal and experiential introduction to the relationship between descriptions of coordinate patterns and graphs in the Cartesian plane. Too often, students don't really "get" the connection between an equation and the graph it produces. It's important for students to understand that graphs represent the set of points whose coordinates satisfy an equation. This activity attempts to foster that understanding.

Thus, any sort of class or group discussion that encourages students to ponder this relationship ("Why do the points 'line up' in such regular ways?" "If you could plot not just five, but *every* point that satisfies the description, what would that look like?") will deepen the experience.

Sketch and Investigate

Q1 In each case, the answer shown depicts *all* possible answers with integer coordinates on the grid provided. The question asks for five answers, so any five of the points shown is a correct response (not to mention the infinite number of correct responses outside the grid!).

a.
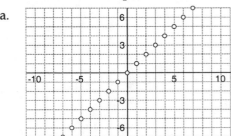

b.
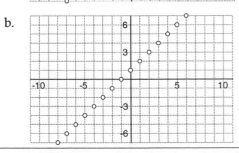

Points "Lining Up" in the Plane

Continued from previous page.

c.
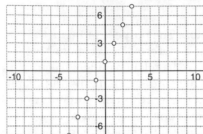

d.
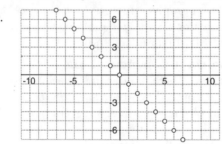

e.
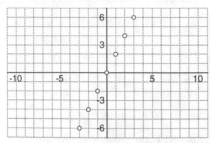

f.
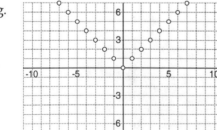

g.
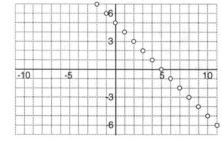

h.
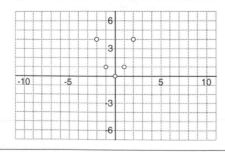

Q2 a. The *y*-coordinate equals the *x*-coordinate.

b. The *y*-coordinate is one less than the *x*-coordinate.

c. The *y*-coordinate is twice the *x*-coordinate. (Or, the *x*-coordinate is one-half the *y*-coordinate.)

d. The *y*-coordinate is two less than twice the *x*-coordinate.

e. The *y*-coordinate is one-third the *x*-coordinate. (Or, the *x*-coordinate is three times the *y*-coordinate.)

f. The *y*-coordinate is always –1 (regardless of the value of the *x*-coordinate).

g. The *y*-coordinate is the opposite of the absolute value of the *x*-coordinate. (An acceptable alternate answer for students not familiar with the term *absolute value* might be "The *y*-coordinate is the 'negative value' of the *x*-coordinate, regardless of whether the *x*-coordinate is positive or negative.")

h. The product of the *y*-coordinate and the *x*-coordinate is 6.

Explore More

1. Q1: a. $y = x$ b. $y = x + 1$ c. $y = 2x$
   d. $y = 2x + 1$ e. $y = -x$ f. $x + y = 5$
   g. $y = |x|$ h. $y = x^2$

   Q2: a. $y = x$ b. $y = x - 1$ c. $y = 2x$
   d. $y = 2x - 2$ e. $y = (1/3)x$ or $x = 3y$
   f. $y = -1$ g. $y = -|x|$ h. $xy = 6$

2. Answers will vary.

   Here's how to set up the Movement button (more detailed instructions are on page 2 of **LineUp.gsp**): Plot the eight destination points using the **Plot Point** command. Select all 16 points in the sketch in the following order: point *A*, point *A*'s destination, point *B*, point *B*'s destination, point *C*, point *C*'s destination, . . . , point *H*, point *H*'s destination. Now, choose **Movement** from the Action Buttons submenu of the Edit menu. Change the speed and label (on the Label panel) if you'd like, and then click OK. Now hide the eight destination points (using the **Hide** command in the Display menu).

The Slope of a Line (page 40)

Student Audience: Pre-algebra/Algebra 1

Prerequisites: Familiarity with the Cartesian plane. Students should know what the *origin* is.

Sketchpad Proficiency: Beginner

Activity Time: 20–30 minutes

Example Sketch: Slope.gsp from the folder 2_Lines. This shows how the sketch should be after step 6. Students could open this sketch and start from step 7, but we recommend *not* doing this as the first six steps aren't difficult and provide a good introduction to Sketchpad.

General Notes: The purpose of this activity is to get a general feel for slope before learning exactly how slope is calculated. The focus, therefore, should be on qualitative relationships, such as how all lines with a positive slope are different from all lines with a negative slope.

Teachers: A good way to test if your students have really internalized the concepts in this activity is to have them model lines using their forearms. Ask the class which arm would be more convenient for modeling lines with a positive slope (left) and which for those with a negative slope (right). Start by having students model slopes of 1 and –1 and remind them that these should be thought of as "points" of reference. Then shout out slope values ("5 … –1 … 0.2 … –1/2 … 0 … –100") and have students quickly approximate them with their arms.

An interesting discussion topic during or after this activity is whether or not there is a biggest or a smallest possible slope for a line.

The Slope Game (page 42) is a good follow-up to this activity.

Sketch and Investigate

Q1 a. A line with a slope of 1 will go up to the right and make angles of 45° with both axes. (Note that the angles wouldn't be 45° if this weren't a *square* coordinate system—in other words, one in which the units along both axes are the same size.)

  b. A line with a slope of –1 will go up to the left and will also make angles of 45° with both axes. (The note from the previous question applies.)

  c. A line with a slope of 0 is perfectly flat—horizontal, in other words.

  d. A line with an undefined slope is perfectly vertical.

  e. Lines with positive slopes always go up to the right and down to the left, regardless of how steep they are.

  f. Lines with negative slopes always go up to the left and down to the right, regardless of how steep they are.

Q2 Lines with a slope greater than 1 are steeper than lines with a slope of 1. Lines with a slope between 0 and 1 are less steep than lines with a slope of 1. (It's helpful to think of lines with a slope of 1 as the "middle case" between steeper and less steep.)

Q3 They are just as steep, but in the opposite direction (one goes up to the right, the other up to the left). A fancy way of expressing this is that the two lines are reflections of each other across the vertical line through their point of intersection.

Q4 The line is translated—in other words, shifted in some direction—but not rotated, so its slope doesn't change and neither does the slope measurement. One way of saying this is that the line is dragged "parallel to itself."

Q5 There are an infinite number of solutions for each blank in the table (why?). Those listed here are the ones that fit in a standard-sized sketch window. Where only one point fits, the two closest points—one in either direction—are listed.

  a. $(1, 2)$, $(2, 4)$, $(-1, -2)$, or $(-2, -4)$

  b. $(3, 0)$ or $(4, -3)$

  c. $(a, 4)$ where a is any x-value; for example, $(3, 4)$ works

  d. $(6, 0)$, $(10, 5)$, or $(-2, -10)$

  e. $(3, b)$ where b is any y-value; for example, $(3, -2)$ works

  f. $(-4, 5)$, $(-7, 13)$, or $(2, -11)$

  g. $(5, 3)$, $(13, 4)$, or $(-11, 1)$

  h. $(2, -5)$, $(0, -12)$, or $(6, 9)$

Explore More

1. Many possible answers. *Angles* are used to describe, among other things, aircraft takeoff paths. *Percentages* are used to describe, among other things, the "grade" of a stretch of road (what this percentage refers to exactly is an interesting question to discuss or research). *Words* are also used, as in "Golly, that's a mighty steep driveway you've got there!"

The Slope Game (page 42)

Student Audience: Pre-algebra/Algebra 1

Prerequisites: Students should have had some introduction to slope, though it isn't necessary for them to know the rise/run definition yet.

Sketchpad Proficiency: Beginner. Students draw, drag, and measure the slopes of lines.

Activity Time: 5–15 minutes. This activity works well as a follow-up to The Slope of a Line.

General Notes: This simple, unassuming game has been a favorite in classrooms and workshops for years. Students really do enjoy trying to "trick" each other with lines that are very close to each other in slope, or the opposite of each other, and this leads to a good learning opportunity.

If this activity is done in the classroom, the teacher may want to prepare by unchecking both choices on the Text panel of Preferences so that points won't automatically show their labels. (Choose **Preferences** in the Edit menu and click on the Text tab.) If there isn't time for this, the teacher can instruct students to do this before starting the activity or instruct them how to show and hide labels (clicking on the object itself with the **Text** tool is the easiest way).

Step 1 says to draw "five different random lines." This means that the lines shouldn't be attached to each other or to the coordinate axes. In other words, students should click in blank space when constructing the lines so that all control points are independent points.

How Slope Is Measured (page 43)

Student Audience: Pre-algebra/Algebra 1

Prerequisites: Though it isn't absolutely necessary, it helps if students know some basics about slope such as the difference between positive and negative slope, what a line with a slope of 1 looks like, and so on. One way to learn these basics is to do the previous two activities: The Slope of a Line and The Slope Game.

Sketchpad Proficiency: Beginner. Students merely drag points in a pre-made sketch.

Activity Time: 25–35 minutes

Required Sketch: **Rise Run.gsp** from the folder **2_Lines**

General Notes: Prior to starting this activity, teachers may wish to initiate a discussion on how one might go about measuring slope. Students might suggest using the angle formed by the line and an axis. This is a good suggestion (and, in fact, this method is sometimes used), but the teacher could note that this doesn't correspond with values already encountered (in the previous two activities, if those were done). The teacher might help the students by pointing out that they will usually know the coordinates of points on the line. The objective, of course, isn't to get students to discover the rule necessarily, but rather to help them appreciate the problem and, subsequently, its solution.

Sketch and Investigate

Q1 The completed table appears as follows (with answers in **bold**):

(x_A, y_A)	(x_B, y_B)	run	rise	slope
(2, 1)	(4, 2)	2	1	0.5
(4, 0)	(5, 3)	**1**	**3**	**3**
(−5, −1)	(−3, 4)	**2**	**5**	**2.5**
(−5, 3)	(5, 4)	**10**	**1**	**0.1**
(2, -3)	**(4, 3)**	2	6	**3**

Q2 The completed table appears as follows (with answers in **bold**):

(x_A, y_A)	(x_B, y_B)	run	rise	slope
(2, 1)	(4, 0)	2	−1	−0.5
(1, −1)	(0, 4)	**−1**	**5**	**−5**
(−3, 6)	(−5, −1)	**−2**	**−7**	**3.5**
(3, 5)	**(−1, 2)**	**−4**	**−3**	**0.75**

Q3 Here are all possible integer answers in the original sketch window (with answers in **bold**):

(x_A, y_A)	(x_B, y_B)	run	rise	slope
(2, 1)	(4, 2)	2	1	0.5
(2, 1)	(6, 3)	4	2	0.5
(2, 1)	(8, 4)	6	3	0.5
(2, 1)	(0, 0)	–2	–1	0.5
(2, 1)	(–2, –1)	–4	–2	0.5
(2, 1)	(–4, –2)	–6	–3	0.5
(2, 1)	(–6, –3)	–8	–4	0.5
(2, 1)	(–8, –4)	–10	–5	0.5

Q4 slope = *rise/run*

Q5 rise = $y_B - y_A$

Q6 run = $x_B - x_A$

Q7 slope = $(y_B - y_A)/(x_B - x_A)$

Explore More

1. The slope is the same regardless of whether you imagine going from *A* to *B* or *B* to *A*. The reason is that *both* the numerator and the denominator of the *slope* equation will be the opposite of what they were before, and these two opposites in effect cancel each other out. Whether you divide a positive number by a negative number or a negative number by a positive number, the result will be negative. Similarly, whether you divide a positive number by a positive number or a negative number by a negative number the result will be positive.

2. For a horizontal line, the *rise* will be 0. Thus, *slope* will equal *rise/run,* which equals 0/*run,* which equals 0. Similarly, for a vertical line, the *run* will be 0. Thus, *slope* will equal *rise/run,* which equals *rise*/0, which is undefined.

3. Briefly, if they had chosen *run/rise,* steeper lines would have smaller slopes and less steep lines would have greater slopes. The definition would still work, but it would be counterintuitive.

Slopes of Parallel and Perpendicular Lines (page 45)

Student Audience: Pre-algebra/Algebra 1

Prerequisites: Students should understand the terms *parallel* and *perpendicular.* Students do not need to be familiar with slope, though this helps.

Sketchpad Proficiency: Beginner. (Students will need greater proficiency to do Explore More 1 and 2.)

Activity Time: 15–25 minutes

Example Sketch: Parallel Perp.gsp from the folder **2_Lines.** This shows how the sketch should be after step 7. Students could open this sketch and start from step 6, but we recommend *not* doing this as the first five steps and step 7 aren't difficult and provide a good introduction to Sketchpad.

General Notes: Teachers may wish to initiate this activity with a simple question, such as "How can you tell whether or not two lines are parallel? How about perpendicular." Even if students do hit upon the idea of using slope, they're unlikely to know exactly how to use slope to test for perpendicularity.

Sketch and Investigate

Q1 The angle measurement approaches 0° (and may even disappear when the slopes are precisely equal).

Q2 If two lines have equal slopes, then the lines are parallel. To verify this, one might *construct* parallel lines using the **Parallel Lines** command and make the necessary measurements.

Q3 Many possible answers. For example, if the product is positive, either both lines have positive slopes or both have negative slopes. Also, if the product is 0, at least one line has a slope of 0.

Q4 The product of the slopes of perpendicular lines is always –1 (as long as one of the lines is not vertical).

Q5 If two lines are perpendicular, one of the slopes must be positive and the other negative. The product of a positive number and a negative number is always a negative number.

Q6 The slope of a vertical line is undefined and the product of an undefined quantity with any other number is also undefined.

Slopes of Parallel and Perpendicular Lines

Continued from previous page.

Explore More

1. With lines constructed to be exactly perpendicular, the slope product calculation should always be exactly –1, regardless of the precision used. (The only exception to this is, of course, when one of the lines is vertical and therefore has an undefined slope.) This should be more convincing than the earlier demonstration, but it still doesn't constitute proof. Why? Because it hasn't been argued conclusively that there couldn't be, for example, some particular slope of one line—say 3.45678—that for some reason doesn't follow the pattern. All we know is that it happened to work for the particular cases we investigated.

2. The angle measurement disappears because its vertex is point *E*. Point *E* is defined as the intersection of the two lines, so when the lines are parallel (and therefore don't intersect) the point ceases to exist.

3. Reciprocals are "flipped" fractions, such as 2/3 and 3/2 or 5 and 1/5 (think of 5 as 5/1). The product of a number and its reciprocal is always 1 since the numerators and denominators all cancel out. The product of a number and its opposite reciprocal can be represented as $(a/b) \cdot (-b/a)$, which can be rewritten as $-1 \cdot (a/b) \cdot (b/a)$, which can be rewritten as $-1 \cdot 1$, which equals –1.

Direct Variation (page 47)

Student Audience: Algebra 1

Prerequisites: None

Sketchpad Proficiency: Intermediate

Activity Time: 35–45 minutes

Example Sketch: Direct Variation.gsp from the folder **2_Lines**. The pages of this document show the activity as it's supposed to be after steps 4, 6, 9, 11, and 12.

General Notes: In this activity, we move from looking at properties of lines (in particular, slope) to generating linear relationships. Before starting, students might discuss what kinds linear relationships they know and how these would look on a graph.

This activity uses a geometric model that generates a linear relationship. It's important to keep focusing on the aspects of the model that relate to properties of lines, such as slope.

This activity can also be seen as a precursor to the activities that follow. Specifically, this activity focuses on lines of the form $y = mx$ (or $y = bx$) and the next activity focuses on lines of the form $y = mx + b$. Thus, any discussions on why this line goes through the origin and how a direct relationship compares to a linear relationship (it's a *type* of linear relationship—a subset, if you will) would be valuable.

Construction Tips

Step 1: If Sketchpad is set to its default Preference settings, points won't be labeled when they are created. Students can either click on points with the **Text** tool to label them (points will label in alphabetical order) or go to the Text panel of Preferences and check For All New Points.

Steps 2, 3, 7, 8, 9 and 10: If the desired command isn't available (it's grayed out, in other words), this means that the wrong objects (or too many objects) have been selected. Click in blank space to deselect all objects and try again.

Step 10: After doing this step, you may want to move the origin down near the bottom of the sketch window. You may also want to move the parallelogram to a relatively clear area of the sketch.

Investigate

Q1 It shows that as the height gets bigger, the area gets bigger, and as the height gets smaller, the slope gets smaller. (Other responses are possible.)

Q2 $A = b \cdot h$

Q3 $A = f(x) = b \cdot x$

Q4 It's the same! To be more precise, it *contains* the path of the plotted point; the function exists in the first and fourth quadrants and the point only plots in the first quadrant.

Q5 Geometric argument: The graph passes through the origin because the area of a parallelogram with height 0 is 0—hence the point (0, 0). Algebraic argument: The graph passes through the origin because when $x = 0$ in $f(x) = b \cdot x$, $f(0) = 0$—hence the point (0, 0).

Q6 The domain should be restricted to $x > 0$ (or possibly $x \geq 0$ if you consider 0 to be a possible height of a parallelogram).

Q7 It means that as one quantity doubles, the other doubles; as one triples or halves, the other triples or halves. For example, the area of a parallelogram with base 3 and height 4 is 12. If you double the height to 8 (and leave the base the same) the area also doubles to 24. The word "proportional" is used because the area and the height are in proportion ($12/4 = 24/8 = 3$—the base!) with the base as the constant of proportionality.

Q8 The length of the base (b) *is* the slope of the graph. "Wide" parallelograms (those with larger bases) will have steeper h versus A graphs. The reason is that every increase in height will add a lot to the area. "Skinny" parallelograms (those with smaller bases) will have more gradual h versus A graphs. The reason is that similar increases in height will add much less to the area.

Explore More

1. To do this, you need to drag point C parallel to $\overline{AB}$. The fact that the point doesn't move (meaning that neither the height nor the area are changing) means that *shearing* a parallelogram doesn't affect its area.

2. The point traces out what appears to be (and is) a parabola. The graph and the trace no longer coincide. The reason this happens is that we are now varying both the height and the base simultaneously, whereas before we were just varying the height (the base remained constant). Variation in one dimension results in a linear graph, whereas variation in two dimensions results in a quadratic graph.

The Slope-Intercept Form of a Line (page 50)

Student Audience: Algebra 1

Prerequisites: Students need to have studied the *rise/run* definition of slope.

Sketchpad Proficiency: Intermediate.

Activity Time: 25–35 minutes

Required Sketch: Slope Intercept.gsp from the folder 2_Lines

Example Sketch: SlopeInt.gsp from the folder 2_Lines. The pages of this document show the activity as it's supposed to be after steps 2 and 5.

Sketch and Investigate

Q1 $y = 1$ when $x = 0$. The point is (0, 1). It makes sense to call this the y-intercept because it's on the y-axis (because its x-coordinate is 0).

Q2 When you plug in 0 for x in $y = mx + b$, you get $y = m(0) + b$, or $y = 0 + b$, or $y = b$.

Q3 The coordinates of the new point are (1, 3). This satisfies the equation because $y = 2(1) + 1 = 2 + 1 = 3$.

Q4 The lines are shown below with several integer points plotted.

a.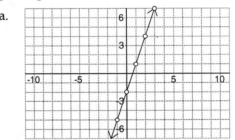

b.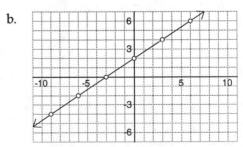

c.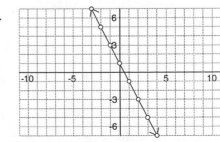

The Slope-Intercept Form of a Line

Continued from previous page.

d.

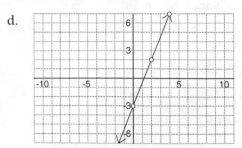

Q5 Lines with a positive *m* go up to the right and down to the left, lines with a negative *m* go down to the right and up to the left, and lines with an *m* of 0 are horizontal.

Q6 As *b* becomes increasingly positive, the line is shifted (translated) up. As *b* becomes increasingly negative, the line is shifted (translated) down.

Q7 This is the family of lines through the point (0, *b*) with any slope. This family can be pictured as resembling an asterisk with an infinite number of lines going through the center point (the *y*-intercept), or a star with an infinite number of rays going out in all directions.

Q8 This is the family of lines with the same slope going through every possible *y*-intercept. This family can be pictured as the infinite set of lines in a plane parallel to a given line.

Q9 a. $y = 2x - 3$ b. $y = -1.5x + 4$
c. $y = 3x + 6$ d. $y = -0.4x - 0.4$
e. $y = 0.5x + 3.5$

Explore More

1. Slope is defined as *rise/run*. For this line, since the *x*-coordinates of both points are the same (3), the *run* is 0. Thus the slope is undefined, since you can't divide by 0. The line can be expressed with the equation $x = 3$, but that's not in slope-intercept form.

2. No, it's not possible. The reason is that every line has a unique *y*-intercept, so there's only one thing *b* can be for a particular line. Similarly, each line has a unique slope, so there's only one thing *m* can be.

The Point-Slope Form of a Line (page 53)

Student Audience: Algebra 1

Prerequisites: Students should already have studied the slope-intercept form of a line.

Sketchpad Proficiency: Beginner/Intermediate. The hardest step is step 3 in which students plot the function (see Construction Tips below). To simplify and shorten the activity, you may want to do this step yourself and have students start at step 4 (or even step 5).

Activity Time: 25–35 minutes

Required Sketch: Point Slope.gsp from the folder 2_Lines

Construction Tips

Step 3: It may be necessary to drag the New Function dialog box by its title bar in order to see the measurements for *m*, *h*, and *k* in the sketch below. Also, there are two other ways to enter *x* into the dialog box: choose x from the Values pop-up menu or type x from the keyboard.

Sketch and Investigate

Q1 The line appears to spin around the point (*h*, *k*).

Q2 This is the family of lines through the point (*h*, *k*) with any slope. This family can be pictured as resembling an asterisk with an infinite number of lines going through the center point (*h*, *k*), or a star with an infinite number of rays going out in all directions.

Q3 These are families of lines with the same slope. The families can be pictured as the infinite set of lines in a plane parallel to a given line. It's interesting that although the two families look the same, they are formed in different ways. Adjusting *h* moves the lines right and left (as can be seen by watching the point (*h*, *k*)) whereas adjusting *k* moves the lines up and down.

Q4 Parameter *h* is the *x*-coordinate of a point on the line. This is the special point that the line spins around when *m* is dragged. Making *h* larger moves the line to the right; making it smaller (or more negative) moves it to the left.

Parameter *k* is the *y*-coordinate of a point on the line. This is the special point that the line spins around when *m* is dragged. Making *k* larger moves the line up; making it smaller (or more negative) moves it down.

Q5 $y = 2(x - 1) + 3$

Q6 a. $y = 2(x + 2) + 1$

　　b. $y = -1(x + 2) + 1$

　　c. $y = 3(x - 0) + 0$ or $y = 3x$

　　d. $y = 0.8(x - 2) + 0$ or $y = 0.8(x - 2)$

　　e. $y = (-1/3)(x - 2) + 3$ or $y = (-1/3)(x + 1) + 4$

　　f. $y = 0(x - 4) + 5$ or $y = 5$

Explore More

1. Slope is defined as *rise/run*. For this line, since the *x*-coordinates of both points are the same (2), the *run* is 0. Thus the slope is undefined, since you can't divide by 0. The line can be expressed with the equation $x = 2$, but that's not in point-slope form.

2. It is possible to express any line (except vertical lines) with an infinite number of equations in point-slope form (or an infinite number of slider configurations in the sketch). The reason is that *h* and *k* aren't unique—any point on the line will do. For example, the line $y = 2(x - 1) + 3$ also goes through the points (2, 5) and (3, 7), so the equations $y = 2(x - 2) + 5$ and $y = 2(x - 3) + 7$ also express this same line (try it out!).

The Standard Form of a Line (page 55)

Student Audience: Algebra 1 / Algebra 2

Prerequisites: Students should probably have already studied the slope-intercept and point-slope forms of a line, though it isn't strictly necessary.

Sketchpad Proficiency: Beginner

Activity Time: 25–35 minutes

Required Sketch: Standard.gsp from the folder 2_Lines

General Notes: After completing this and the previous "... Form of a Line" activities, students should have a good understanding of the three forms and what information each provides. But it's important to emphasize that the three forms can all describe a single line.

Thus, a good way to start this activity might be with a discussion on why there are so many forms. ("Lines are very important . . . Mathematicians have developed different ways of describing them depending on what information they have and what information they need . . . ")

Similarly, a good way to end this activity, and provide a wrap-up for all three activities, might be to ask students to compare and contrast three equivalent equations, such as $y = (2/3)x + 2$, $2x - 3y = -6$, and $y = (2/3)(x - 3) + 4$. Students might then be asked to convert equations in one form into the other two, or to decide which form is most appropriate for a given set of information.

Sketch and Investigate

Q1 From left to right: 3, 2, 1, 0.5, −6, −2.

Q2 $(x_{int})(A) = (C)$ where x_{int} is the *x*-coordinate of the *x*-intercept. This holds for all values of *A* except 0, for which there's no *x*-intercept.

Q3 From left to right: 6, 4, 2, 1, −12, −4.

Q4 The relationship between *B* and the *y*-intercept is the same as that between *A* and the *x*-intercept: namely, $(y_{int})(B) = (C)$ where y_{int} is the *y*-coordinate of the *y*-intercept. This holds for all values of *B* except 0, for which there's no *y*-intercept.

Q5 $x_{int} = C/A$; $y_{int} = C/B$; slope $= -(A/B)$

Q6 a. $3x - 4y = 3$　　　b. $-2x + 5y = 10$

　　c. $x + 2y = 4$　　　d. $5x - 3y = 0$

　　e. $-2x + 4y = 2$

Solving Systems of Equations (page 57)

Student Audience: Algebra 1/Algebra 2

Prerequisites: Students should be at least somewhat familiar with equations of lines. Previous experience with graphing on Sketchpad's coordinate grid would be helpful, as would experience with distance/time graphs.

Sketchpad Proficiency: Intermediate

Activity Time: 30–40 minutes

Example Sketch: Systems.gsp from the folder 2_Lines. The pages of this document show the activity as it's supposed to be after steps 2, 4, 5, 7, and Q6.

Construction Tips

Step 4: Make sure that students construct a line, not a line segment. To attach the line firmly to both points, click the **Line** tool directly on both points, one after the other. You can also select both points and use the **Line** command from the Construct menu.

Step 5: Some possible ordered pairs for Torrance's run are (0, 0.5), (9, 1.5), and (4.5, 1).

Sketch and Investigate

Q1 Many possible answers. In one minute, Claire runs 0.25 km. Thus, one possible ordered pair is (1, 0.25). Since it takes her four minutes to run 1 km, another possibility is (4, 1). At time 0, she hasn't gone anywhere, so (0, 0) is another possibility. Others are (8, 2), (12, 3), and (2, 0.5).

Q2 See Q1.

Q3 The origin—(0, 0)—represents Claire's starting point because when no time has elapsed (zero minutes) she's not yet gone anywhere (0 km).

Q4 The point of intersection of the lines. At this point, both Claire and Torrance have raced the same amount of time and are the same distance from the starting line.

Q5 The coordinates of the point of intersection are (3.6, 0.9). This means that 3.6 minutes (or 3 minutes, 36 seconds) after Claire and Torrance start racing, they are in the same place. This place is 0.9 km from Claire's starting point and 0.4 km from where Torrance started.

Q6 The system of equations is:

$$y = 0.25x$$
$$y = 0.\overline{1}x + 0.5 \ \text{ or } \ y = (1/9)x + 0.5$$

Q7 The number 0.25 in the first equation represents Claire's running rate of 0.25 km per minute (equivalent to 1 km every four minutes.) The number $0.\overline{1}$ (= 1/9) in the second equation represents Torrance's running rate of $0.\overline{1}$ kpm (or 1 km every nine minutes.) The number 0.5 in the second equation represents Torrance's half-kilometer head start.

Q8 Answers vary. Below are a sample sketch and a response. Depending on the student's algebra skills, they may want to prove that the runners meet at the times and places indicated by their sketch. Remember, Sketchpad's values are rounded, so the algebraic answers may be slightly different from the graphical answers. Increasing precision to thousandths in the Preferences dialog box may help.

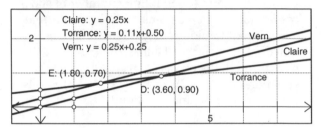

Name: Vern

Speed: 0.25 km/min

Starting point: He has a 0.25 km head start.

When and where this racer meets Torrance): Vern passes Torrance after 1.8 minutes (1 minute, 48 seconds). They are each 0.7 km from the starting point (where Claire started).

When and where this racer meets Claire: They never meet, since Vern runs at the same speed as Claire and they start in different places.

Equation that models this racer's trip:
$$y = 0.25x + 0.25$$

Explore More

1. For a pair of lines to intersect more than once, they must be *coincident* (identical) and intersect at infinitely many points. This corresponds to the situation in which two runners start at the same place (side-by-side?) and run at the same speed.

   Any pair of parallel lines will do for a system with no solution. This corresponds to the situation in which two runners start at different places and run at the same speed.

For three distinct lines, the maximum number of points of intersection is 3. For four lines, the maximum is 6. For five lines, it's 10. Finally, for n distinct lines, the maximum number of points of intersection is $n(n-1)/2$.

2. The following types of solutions are possible: two solutions (the line is a secant of the circle), one solution (the line is tangent to the circle), or no solutions (the line and circle don't intersect).

   Two circles could intersect once, twice, not at all, or infinitely many times. So a system of equations modeling two circles could have one, two, zero, or infinitely many solutions.

3. By using the **Line** tool, we ended up with lines extending in both directions from the starting points. This would imply that the runners were running before the starting time, approaching the starting point from the opposite direction. Using the **Ray** tool, we can have the rays start at the racers' starting points and only go forward in time and direction.

   There are several other ways in which the model is inaccurate, or at least idealized. For example, people can't start at their full speed—there has to be at least a short period of acceleration before their speeds become constant. On the graph, this would appear as an upward sloping curve as opposed to a straight line.

The Absolute Value Function and the "V-Graph" (page 60)

Student Audience: Algebra 1/Algebra 2

Prerequisites: Students should probably be familiar with the term *absolute value* before attempting this activity, even though it starts with a brief introduction to this concept. Students should be familiar with slope and line graphing in general, and familiarity with the point-slope form of lines in particular is helpful.

Sketchpad Proficiency: Intermediate. Students may need a little help entering equations into the New Function dialog box.

Activity Time: 25–35 minutes

Required Sketch: VGraph.gsp from the folder 2_Lines

General Notes: In and of itself, how the absolute value function affects graphs probably isn't the most important thing for most Algebra 1 students to learn. But, there are two good, practical reasons for doing this activity: first, it reinforces students' understanding of the point-slope form of lines (the role of point (h, k) becomes even more apparent), and second, it prepares students for the vertex form of parabolas.

It's important for students to actually predict what the absolute value graphs will look like before they graph them. Just by plotting a few points—such as $(-2, 2)$, $(0, 0)$, and $(2, 2)$—they can start to see *why* the absolute value does what it does to the graph.

Sketch and Investigate

Q1 The graphs are identical to the right of $x = 2$. To the left of $x = 2$, the graphs are reflections about the x-axis. Another way of describing this is that the part of $y = 2x - 4$ that was below the x-axis has been flipped above the x-axis. $y = 2x - 4$ is a line whereas $y = |2x - 4|$ is shaped like a V. The range of $y = 2x - 4$ is all real numbers whereas the range of $y = |2x - 4|$ is all real numbers greater than or equal to 0.

The Absolute Value Function and the "V-Graph"

Continued from previous page.

A Family of Absolute Value Graphs

Q2 The sign of m determines whether the V opens up or down or is flat: graphs of equations with positive m's open up, with negative m's open down, and with $m = 0$ are totally flat. The greater the absolute value of m, the "skinnier" the graph; the lesser the absolute value of m, the "wider" the graph. The slope of the right half of the V always equals m while the slope of the left half of the V always equals $-m$.

Q3 Quite simply! The coordinates of the vertex are, in fact, (h, k).

Q4 a. $y = 2|x + 1| + 2$ b. $y = -1.5|x - 2| + 3$
      c. $y = 3|x + 3| - 1$ d. $y = (2/3)|x| - 8/3$
      e. $y = -1|x - 2| + 4$ f. $y = -2.5|x - 2| + 5$

Explore More

1. Let's say you graph two equations: $y = f(x)$ and $y = |f(x)|$. Where the first graph is below the x-axis, it will be reflected across (above) the x-axis in the second graph. Where the first graph is above the x-axis, the second graph will be identical.

Swans and Giraffes: Introducing Linear Programming (page 62)

Student Audience: Algebra 1/Algebra 2

Prerequisites: Students should be very fluent with linear equations, simultaneous equations, and word problems.

Sketchpad Proficiency: Beginner

Activity Time: 40–50 minutes

Required Sketch: Origami.gsp from the folder 2_Lines

Assigning Variables and Writing the Profit Equation

Q1 Profit = $4x + 6y$

Q2 The closer point R is to the origin, the lesser the profit. (In fact, the profit is zero when R is at the origin.) The farther up and to the right, the greater the profit.

Q3 It makes sense to have point R snap to locations with integer coordinates because Rei can only make whole numbers of swans and giraffes. It doesn't make sense, in other words, to consider her making 3.71 swans or 4.2 giraffes.

Also, it doesn't make sense to consider her making negative numbers of swans or giraffes, which is why only the first quadrant and positive axes are reasonable locations for point R. This can be expressed by the constraint inequalities $x \geq 0$ and $y \geq 0$.

Setting Up the Constraint Inequalities

Q4 The paper constraint is satisfied only within (and on the perimeter of) the triangle bounded by the two axes and the red line. Within this region, the profit is greatest at the upper-left corner, or $(0, 16)$. This makes sense since, without the time constraint, the greatest profit would be made by using all 16 pieces of paper to make giraffes.

Q5 $3x$ = how long it takes Rei to make x swans
$6y$ = how long it takes Rei to make y giraffes

Q6 $3x + 6y \leq 60$

Q7 In the upper-right (green) region, neither constraint is met. In the light blue region, the time constraint is met and the paper constraint isn't. In the orange region, the paper constraint is met and the time constraint isn't. In the lower-left (yellow) region, both constraints are met.

Finding the Maximum

Q8 Rei should make 12 giraffes and 4 swans for a profit of $72 dollars.

Explore More

1. This increases the size of the feasible region a bit, moving the upper-right vertex a little down and to the right. Rei would be able to make a greater profit with this change. In fact, increasing the number of pieces of paper Rei has would increase her profit up to the point at which she has 20 pieces. Having more than 20 pieces of paper wouldn't make any difference (because of the time constraint).

2. Each additional piece of paper increases her profit by $2 up to a maximum of $80 profit with 20 pieces of paper.

3. The line $y < 8$ corresponds to the constraint "Rei didn't want to make any more than eight giraffes." This is a region to the left of a vertical line that cuts the original feasible region into a smaller trapezoidal region. The maximum profit for this situation is $68, occurring once again at the upper-right vertex of the feasible region: eight giraffes and six swans.

4. The profit line represents all of the combinations of giraffes and swans—x_R and y_R—that give the same profit. You can see this by dragging point R along the line (the profit doesn't change). With the profit line way up and to the right, you get a very large profit but R doesn't pass through the feasible region. With the profit line cutting through the feasible region, R can take on feasible values but the profit isn't at its greatest. Only when the profit line just barely touches the feasible region—at a corner point— is the profit maximized.

An Ant's Progress: Modeling Linear Motion in Time (page 66)

Student Audience: Algebra 1/Algebra 2

Prerequisites: Students should probably have a good understanding of lines—slope, slope-intercept and point-slope forms—before trying this activity, even though it doesn't specifically rely on any of these concepts.

Sketchpad Proficiency: Beginner. Mostly students drag points and push buttons in a pre-made sketch. Students may need a little help editing equations later in the activity.

Activity Time: 30–40 minutes

Required Sketch: Ants Progress.gsp from the folder **2_Lines**

General Notes: Even though this activity covers a topic—parametric equations of lines—that isn't typically taught in Algebra 1, it is an accessible, valuable, and fun activity for students to do. It's especially valuable if connections are made between the parametric equations and the slope-intercept and point-slope forms of lines.

Investigate

Q1

t:	0	1	2	3	4
x:	−4	−1	2	5	8
y:	−5	−3	−1	1	3

Q2 The following points should be plotted: (−4, −5), (−1, −3), (2, −1), (5, 1), and (8, 3)

Q3 $x = −2 + 2t$ and $y = 0 + 1t$ (or $y = t$)

Sketch

Q4 The ant crosses the y-axis after 1 minute and 20 seconds ($t = 4/3$). It crosses the x-axis after 2 minute and 30 seconds ($t = 5/2$).

To find the first answer, set x equal to 0 in the first equation and solve for t. Similarly, to find the second answer, set y equal to 0 in the second equation and solve for t.

Using these values of t, we can also find the x- and y-intercepts. When $t = 4/3$, $y = −7/3$, and when $t = 5/2$, $x = 7/2$. Thus, −7/3 is the y-intercept and 7/2 is the x-intercept.

An Ant's Progress: Modeling Linear Motion in Time

Continued from previous page.

Q5 The equation Sketchpad gives is $y = 0.67x - 2.33$, which is a rounded version of $y = (2/3)x - (7/3)$, or $2x - 3y = 7$. The y-intercept, $-7/3$, is the value of y when $x = 0$. This can be computed using the first parametric equation. The value $2/3$ is the slope. Its denominator, 3, is the *run* and corresponds with the coefficient of t in the first equation. The numerator, 2, is the *rise* and corresponds with the coefficient of t in the second equation.

Q6 The most likely answer is $x = 5 - 12t$ and $y = 1 + 18t$. This represents a motion six times as fast as the original motion. If a student assumes that the ant must travel at the same speed as before, he or she has anticipated the next question and would get that answer. In general, any answer in the form $x = 5 - (2a)t$ and $y = 1 + (3a)t$, $a > 0$, is correct here.

Q7 The equations are $x = 5 - 2t$ and $y = 1 + 3t$. To see that this is the same speed as in the previous motion, consider that there the ant went 3 units right and 2 units up per second, whereas here it's going 2 units left and 3 units up per second. By the way, it will take the ant 6 seconds to reach $(-7, 19)$.

Where Are the Giant Ants? (page 73)

Student Audience: Pre-algebra/Algebra 1

Prerequisites: Students need to understand the concepts of *area* and *ratio*. *Dilate* may be a new term that needs more explanation than is provided in the activity itself. Students may also need to be introduced to the term *corresponding side*.

Sketchpad Proficiency: Intermediate. This activity involves quite a bit of work in Sketchpad. Although clear instructions are provided for every step, novice Sketchpad users may find the activity quite challenging. For this reason, or to save time, you can start in the middle of the activity on one of the pages of the sketch **Giant Ants.gsp**.

Activity Time: 30–40 minutes

Example Sketch: **Giant Ants.gsp** from the folder **3_Quads**. The pages of this document show the activity as it's supposed to be after steps 4, 7, 10, 11, and 13.

General Notes: This activity is intended to introduce students to quadratic relationships and to contrast quadratic with linear relationships both numerically and graphically. Comparing the sizes of similar shapes will give students insight into one of the core ideas in the form and growth of animals.

Since students have often studied only linear relationships, teachers might introduce this activity by asking students what other types of relationships they know about or can imagine and how those relationships compare with linear ones.

Students are almost always surprised that length and area (or volume) do not grow in the same way. In order to confront their beliefs about growth, students should be encouraged to make and express their predictions prior to verifying them with Sketchpad.

This activity can provoke much class discussion and is well suited to classroom sharing. For instance, each student might choose to begin with a different type or shape of polygon. By comparing their own results with those of classmates, students will gain a better appreciation of the quadratic growth of area for *any* shape. This will help them construct arguments for supporting the case of more "non-geometric" shapes, such as inkblots or amoebas.

Though the primary focus of this activity is length and area relationships, students might also be encouraged to investigate volume and surface area (what is the relationship between length and volume, or between surface area and volume?). This might prove more tractable with rectangles and boxes than polygons. Once students have investigated area and talked about volume, they might also be able to predict what happens in higher dimensions.

Construction Tips

Step 4: Use the **Arrow** tool in this step.

Step 7: Again, use the Arrow tool in this step. The simplest way to select the entire figure is probably to use a selection marquee. Students may wish to give the new interior a different color from the Display | Color submenu to distinguish it from the original interior.

Step 8: Make sure to deselect all objects before selecting the two segments. Then measure the ratio using the Ratio command in the Measure menu, just as in step 4.

Step 9: Again, deselect all objects before selecting the interiors. To select an interior, just click on it (and not on its sides or vertex points).

Step 10: Students may need to drag the Calculator by its title bar in order to see and click on the perimeter measurements in the sketch below. To make the calculation, just click on the scaled interior's perimeter measurement, the divide symbol in the Calculator, the original interior's perimeter measurement, and finally OK.

Step 12: Students may wish to hide the grid (by choosing **Hide Grid** from the Graph menu), move the origin, and otherwise rearrange objects in the sketch to clean things up.

Sketch and Investigate

Q1 They are the same. (If they aren't, check that the sides chosen were really *corresponding* sides and that they were selected in the proper order—scaled polygon, then original polygon.)

Q2 The area ratio is the square of the side-length ratio. For example, if the side-length ratio is 3 (3:1), the area ratio will be 9 (9:1). In terms of the "flat elephant," if you double its waist size, you will quadruple the area of its skin.

Q3 The graph makes sense because it appears to be a parabola (the graph of a quadratic function) and the relationship graphed is quadratic, as discussed in the previous question.

If students are too inexperienced with parabolas and quadratics to make this connection, they still may be able to see that the area ratio *grows faster* than the side-length ratio as the scale factor gets bigger. This corresponds to the upward turn of the parabolic trace.

Explore More

1. The same relationship holds with any two-dimensional shape: The ratio of the areas of the similar shapes is the square of the side lengths. Try superimposing a grid on the lumpy shape to see why this holds true.

2. The ratio of the volumes of similar solids is the *cube* of the ratio of side lengths.

3. The ratio of the perimeters of the similar shapes is the same as the ratio of the side lengths.

4. An animal that is twice as long, tall, and wide as another similarly shaped animal will have four times the surface area (skin) and eight times the volume. For this reason, relatively small evolutionary size increases place great demands on the overall system. The legs of the giant ant would never be able to support the mass of its body.

Parabolas in Vertex Form (page 76)

Student Audience: Algebra 1/Algebra 2

Prerequisites: Students need to understand the basic idea of a function and the role that the variables x and y play in the equation and graph of a function. Solving simple linear equations for one unknown after substituting given values for other unknowns is also part of this activity.

Sketchpad Proficiency: Intermediate/advanced if the activity is done as written. If a simpler (and shorter) activity is desired, use the sketch **ParabVtx.gsp** from the folder **3_Quads** and start on the second page of the activity.

Activity Time: 40–50 minutes. The activity is much shorter (20–35 minutes) if you use the alternate sketch **ParabVtx.gsp** and start on the second page of the activity.

Required Sketch: Vertex Form.gsp from the folder **3_Quads**

General Notes: The material covered in this activity is also covered in the next—Exploring Parabolas in Vertex Form. But there it's covered in a more open-ended way, which may or may not suit some students or some classes better.

Teachers may wish to draw attention to the similarities between this equation form for the parabola and the point-slope form of a line (as well as the formula used in the "V-Graph" activity, if they've done that). A good topic of discussion is whether or not there's a notion of slope with parabolas. If so, how is it different from the slope of a line? If not, what does a control?

Sketch and Investigate

Q1 Many possible answers.

This is a good calculator activity for substituting an x-value into the right side of a function to determine a y-value. Any small discrepancy is due to Sketchpad's rounding (depending on the Precision settings in Preferences).

Q2 If a is positive, the parabola opens up; if a is negative, the parabola opens down. The larger the absolute value of a, the "narrower" the parabola. The closer a is to zero, the "wider" the parabola.

Q3 The coordinates of the vertex are (h, k).

Q4 The parabola moves right and left as h changes (right as h gets bigger, left as it gets smaller). The parabola moves up and down as k changes (up as k gets bigger, down as it gets smaller).

Q5 a. $y = 5(x - 1)^2 - 1$
   b. $y = 0.5(x + 4)^2 - 3$
   c. $y = -0.5(x - 5)^2 + 2$
   d. $y = 2(x - 2)^2 - 2$
   e. $y = 4(x + 1)^2 + 3$

It's very important that students find the equations of these parabolas using paper and pencil calculations and use Sketchpad to check their answers. Slider accuracy may account for small differences.

Q6 $x = 3; x = h$

Q7 $(1, 9)$

Explore More

1. Since $x = h$ is the axis of symmetry, $(2h - s, t)$ is the symmetry point.

2. The axis of symmetry is perpendicular to the x-axis and passes through the vertex (h, k).

Exploring Parabolas in Vertex Form (page 79)

Student Audience: Algebra 1/Algebra 2

Prerequisites: None in particular. Some familiarity with parabolas and with graphical transformations (such as in the various line form activities in Chapter 2) would help.

Sketchpad Proficiency: Beginner. Students manipulate sliders in a pre-made sketch.

Activity Time: 20–40 minutes. Depends on how many questions are explored, whether answers are written or discussed, how detailed the answers are, and so on.

Required Sketch: Explore Vertex.gsp from the folder 3_Quads

General Notes: The previous activity—Parabolas in Vertex Form—is concerned with the same subject matter as this activity, but approaches it in a much different way. That activity uses a more traditional, step-by-step approach, and it focuses exclusively on the vertex form. This activity uses a more open-ended approach and builds toward the vertex form from much more basic parabola forms. Which approach is more appropriate depends on the particular students and the particular class involved.

Questions to ponder, discuss, or write about

Q1 The integer points visible in the sketch window are (0, 0), (1, 1), (–1, 1), (2, 4), (–2, 4), (3, 9), and (–3, 0). Four other integer points not visible but on the parabola are (4, 16), (–4, 16), (5, 25), and (–5, 25). (Many other answers are possible for the second part of this question.)

Q2 It must be of the form $y = ax^2$. In vertex form, a parabola with vertex (0, 0) is written as $y = a(x – 0)^2 + 0$, which simplifies to $y = ax^2$.

Q3 They are all symmetrical across the y-axis. This is because the square of a number is the same as the square of its opposite. For example, if $y = 2x^2$, both (3, 18) and (–3, 18) are on the graph because $3^2 = (–3)^2$. These two points are reflections of each other across the y-axis. Functions that have this property, $f(–x) = f(x)$, are called *even* functions.

Q4 Point $(–a, b)$ is also on the parabola.

Q5 In every case, parabolas with positive a's open upward and parabolas with negative a's open downward.

Q6 They become flat, horizontal lines.

Q7 Coefficient m controls the slopes of lines and a controls something for parabolas that's very much like slope, namely how "skinny" (steep) or "wide" (flat) a parabola is. In both cases, the sign affects which direction the graphs go to the right: positive a's and m's mean the graph goes up to the right and negative a's and m's mean the graph goes down to the right. But whether the graph goes up or down to the left is different in the two cases: with lines, the line will always go the opposite direction to the left as it goes to the right, and parabolas will always go the same way to the right as to the left.

Q8 It makes sense because the y-coordinate at $x = 1$ is a. To see this, just plug in 1 for x in $y = ax^2$—you get $y = a$.

Q9 The equation of the axis of symmetry for both $y = ax^2$ and $y = ax^2 + k$ is $x = 0$. The equation of the axis of symmetry for $y = a(x – h)^2 + k$ is $x = h$.

Q10 Dragging h and k results in horizontal and vertical translations respectively. Dragging a results in a dilation.

Explore More

1. One way to do this is to construct the vertex by selecting h and k in that order and choosing **Plot As (x, y)** from the Graph menu. Now select the newly plotted point and the x-axis and choose **Perpendicular Line** from the Construct menu. Another way would be to choose **Plot New Function** from the Graph menu, choose **x = f(y)** from the Equations pop-up menu, then click on h's measurement and click OK.

Parabolas in Factored Form (page 81)

Student Audience: Algebra 1/Algebra 2

Prerequisites: Students need to understand the basic idea of a function and the role that the variables x and y play in the equation and graph of a function. Solving simple linear equations for one unknown after substituting given values for other unknowns is also part of this activity.

Sketchpad Proficiency: Intermediate/advanced if the activity is done as written. If a simpler (and shorter) activity is desired, use the sketch **ParabFct.gsp** from the folder **3_Quads** and start on the second page of the activity.

Activity Time: 40–50 minutes. The activity is much shorter (20–35 minutes) if you use the alternate sketch **ParabFct.gsp** and start on the second page of the activity.

Required Sketch: **Factored Form.gsp** from the folder **3_Quads**

General Notes: As with all of the Parabolas in Such-and-Such Form activities, it's important that students understand that a parabola is a parabola regardless of what form its equation is written in. Any parabola can be written in many different forms, most of which don't have names and don't convey useful information. The forms we study are the ones that convey special information about the parabolas they describe.

That being said, factored form is different than any other form studied in this book (including the various forms of linear equations) in that *not all parabolas can be expressed in factored form*. Those that can't are those that don't cross or touch the x-axis. A good way to introduce this activity, then, might be to discuss the different types of parabolas in terms of whether they have 0, 1, or 2 distinct real roots. If students have studied the discriminant, this would be a good opportunity to remind them of that.

Sketch and Investigate

Q1 This is a good calculator activity for substituting an x-value into the right side of a function to determine a y-value. Any small discrepancy is due to Sketchpad's rounding (depending on the Precision settings in Preferences).

Exploring Families of Parabolas

Q2 If a is positive, the parabola opens up; if a is negative, the parabola opens down. The larger the absolute value of a, the "narrower" the parabola. The closer a is to zero, the "wider" the parabola.

Q3 The two points that remain fixed when dragging a are the two x-intercepts. One x-intercept exactly matches the value of the p slider, while the other x-intercept exactly matches the value of the q slider.

Q4 Dragging the p slider changes the x-intercept that matches the p-value. Dragging the q slider changes the other x-intercept to match the q-value.

Q5 A parabola with two equal roots has its vertex on the x-axis. Such roots are called *double roots*.

Q6 a. $y = 0.04(x + 4)(x - 6)$
     b. $y = 2(x + 5)(x - 1)$
     c. $y = 0.3(x - 0)(x + 3)$ or $y = 0.3x(x + 3)$
     d. $y = 1(x - 3)(x + 1)$ or $y = (x - 3)(x + 1)$
     e. $y = 2(x + 4)(x - 1)$

It is very important that students find the equations of these parabolas using paper and pencil calculations and use Sketchpad to check their answers. Slider accuracy may account for small differences.

Q7 The ball will land 120 feet away. The equation is $y = (1/180)(x - 0)(x - 120)$ or $y = (x/180)(x - 120)$

Explore More

1. Because of the symmetry parabolas exhibit, the x-coordinate of the vertex is the average of the two roots, or $(p + q)/2$. To find the y-coordinate of the vertex, plug this expression in for x in the original equation:

$$y = a\left(\frac{p + q}{2} - p\right)\left(\frac{p + q}{2} - q\right)$$

which simplifies to

$$y = \frac{-a}{4}(p - q)^2$$

3. The vertex will trace out a parabola whose vertex is at $(q, 0)$, opens the opposite direction of the given parabola, and is the same shape. The equation is $y = -a(x - q)(x - q)$ or $y = -a(x - q)^2$.

Parabolas in Standard Form (page 84)

Student Audience: Algebra 1/Algebra 2

Prerequisites: Students need to understand the basic idea of a function and the role that the variables x and y play in the equation and graph of a function. Solving simple linear equations for one unknown after substituting given values for other unknowns is also part of this activity.

Sketchpad Proficiency: Intermediate/advanced if the activity is done as written. If a simpler (and shorter) activity is desired, use the sketch **ParabStd.gsp** from the folder **3_Quads** and start on the second page of the activity.

Activity Time: 40–50 minutes. The activity is shorter (20–35 minutes) if you use the alternate sketch **ParabStd.gsp** and start on the second page of the activity.

Required Sketch: Standard Form.gsp from the folder **3_Quads**

General Notes: As with all of the Parabolas in Such-and-Such Form activities, it's important that students understand that a parabola is a parabola regardless of what form its equation is written in. Any parabola can be written in many different forms, most of which don't have names and don't convey useful information. The forms we study are the ones that convey special information about the parabolas they describe.

Sketch and Investigate

Q1 This is a good calculator activity for substituting an x-value into the right side of a function to determine a y-value. Any small discrepancy is due to Sketchpad's rounding (depending on the Precision settings in Preferences).

Q2 If a is positive, the parabola opens up; if a is negative, the parabola opens down. The larger the absolute value of a, the "narrower" the parabola. The closer a is to zero, the "wider" the parabola.

Q3 Changing parameters a and b has no effect on the y-intercept. The value of parameter c and the y-intercept match exactly.

Q4 Adjusting c's slider moves the parabola up and down. The transformation is a vertical translation.

Q5 The shape of the parabola stays constant, but the axis of symmetry and both the x- and y-coordinates of the vertex change. The path of the vertex is itself a parabola.

Q6 Many possible answers. For example, each of the following has an axis of symmetry of $x = 2$: $y = 1x^2 - 4x + 13$, $y = -1x^2 + 4x - 10$, and $y = 3x^2 - 12x + 127$. (Note that the value of c is irrelevant in every case—it doesn't affect the axis of symmetry.)

Q7 a. $y = 0.5x^2 - 2x + 4$
   b. $y = 2x^2 + 8x + 11$
   c. $y = 0.25x^2 - 0.5x + 3.75$
   d. $y = -0.5x^2 + 3.5x - 4$

It is very important that students find the equations of these parabolas using paper and pencil calculations and use Sketchpad to check their answers. Slider accuracy may account for small differences.

Explore More

1. One approach is as follows: Use the Calculator to calculate the x-coordinate of one of the x-intercepts using the quadratic formula. Use the **New Parameter** command from the Graph menu to create a parameter of 0. Use the **Plot As (x, y)** command to plot the x-intercept (using the 0 parameter for its y-coordinate). Now measure the distance from the x-intercept to the axis of symmetry using the **Distance** command in the Measure menu. Compare the result with the result you get when calculating the value of the second part of the quadratic formula.

Parabolas: A Geometric Approach
(page 87)

Student Audience: Algebra 1/Algebra 2

Prerequisites: This activity works best if students have already been learning about parabolas from an algebraic perspective, but it would work as a first introduction to parabolas (except, perhaps, for Explore More question 2).

Sketchpad Proficiency: Intermediate

Activity Time: 30–45 minutes depending on students' Sketchpad proficiency.

Example Sketch: Geo Parabolas.gsp from the folder **3_Quads**. The pages of this document show the activity as it's supposed to be after steps 4, 6, 9, 11, 14, and 15.

General Notes: A good way to introduce this activity might be to talk a little history. Parabolas have been studied for over 2000 years, but the algebraic equations students have explored in the last four activities have only been known about for the past 500 years or so. How did people describe and define parabolas before? How were they drawn without coordinate geometry? Where do parabolas come from? (sections of cones). This kind of historical perspective may help students appreciate the true power of the algebraic equations.

Construction Tips

Step 2: Holding the shift key while drawing the line helps keep it horizontal.

Step 3: Click the first time on the line itself (though not on one of its control points). The line will be highlighted before you click if the tool is positioned properly.

Step 5: Use the **Arrow** tool in this step.

Step 7: Refer to step 6 for a reminder how to do this.

Step 11: Make sure only point *F* is selected here. To deselect all objects, click in blank space.

Step 12: Traces will gradually fade because of the Preference setting made in step 1. If you prefer that traces not fade, uncheck Fade Traces Over Time on the Color panel of Preferences. To clear traces from the screen, choose **Erase Traces** from the Display menu.

Step 13: Again, make sure only *F* is selected.

Sketch and Investigate

Q1 It's the same distance from either endpoint. This is a theorem from geometry and can be proven, but for our purposes it's probably okay just to leave this up to students' common sense.

Q2 The two length measurements always equal each other. (This should confirm the students' conjectures from Q1.) The length of segment *FC* is the distance from *F* to the directrix and the length of *FD* is the distance of *F* to the focus. Point *F*, then, fits the definition from the activity's Introduction and is therefore on the parabola defined by the given focus and directrix.

Q3 The farther point *C* is from the directrix, the wider the parabola; the closer, the skinnier.

Q4 When point *C* is below the directrix, the parabola opens downward.

Explore More

1. Select the focus and the directrix and choose **Perpendicular Line** from the Construct menu. Click on the spot where this new line intersects the directrix to construct the point of intersection there. Hide the line and then construct a segment between the focus and the new point. Construct the midpoint of this segment using the **Midpoint** command in the Construct menu. This point is the vertex of the parabola.

Building Headlights and Satellite Dishes (page 90)

Student Audience: Algebra 1/Algebra 2

Prerequisites: This activity works best as a follow-up to the previous activity, Parabolas: A Geometric Approach.

Sketchpad Proficiency: Intermediate/Advanced

Activity Time: 40–50 minutes

Required Sketch: Reflector.gsp from the folder **3_Quads** (only required if students didn't do the previous activity and therefore can't use their sketch from that activity)

Example Sketch: Satellite.gsp from the folder **3_Quads**. The pages of this document show the activity as it's supposed to be after steps 3, 5, 6, 9, 10, and 12.

General Notes: One way to introduce this activity would be to ask students what shape a "burning mirror"—a mirror designed to reflect the sun's rays to one point—should be. Why would a straight line (flat mirror) be a bad choice? Students may be interested to know that Diocles discovered—and used—the answer to this question c. 200 B.C. Diocles was improving on work done a century earlier by Archimedes who, as legend has it, used burning mirrors to set the Roman fleet ablaze as it entered Syracuse harbor. Diocles' principle is still used today in solar-powered steam generators. (See Toomer, G.J., *Diocles on Burning Mirrors.* New York: Springer Verlag, 1976.)

Sketch and Investigate

Q1 When the light source is at the focus, the rays will reflect parallel to each other.

Q2 Place the sensor at the focus of the three-dimensional parabola (called a *parabaloid*). The signals coming in roughly parallel to the direction the dish is facing will reflect right to the sensor whereas all other signals will bounce and miss the sensor.

Explore More

1. One example would be the parabolic microphones often seen on the sidelines of football games and used to catch conversation in the huddle. These work basically the same way a satellite dish works: Sound waves coming in roughly parallel to the direction the device is aimed bounce toward the microphone, which is located at the focus. Sound waves from other directions bounce harmlessly away.

The Circumference Function (page 97)

Student Audience: Pre-algebra/Algebra 1

Prerequisites: Students should know the basics about circles, namely, what diameter and circumference are. They also should have had at least some basic introduction to functions.

Sketchpad Proficiency: Intermediate

Activity Time: 40–50 minutes. This can really vary depending on the students' Sketchpad proficiency as this is a pretty construction-heavy activity. To shorten the activity, use the example sketch **Circumference.gsp** and have students start the activity at step 5.

Example Sketch: Circumference.gsp from the folder **4_Functions**. The pages of this document show the activity as it's supposed to be after steps 4, 6, Q3, Q4, and Q6.

General Notes: One of the interesting things about this activity is the relationship between *formulas* and *functions*. Most students at this level know the formula $C = \pi \cdot D$, and most can graph the line $y = 3x$ or $y = 3.14x$ or even $y = \pi x$. Yet very few are able to recognize the first "formula" as being equivalent to the final "equation." In this activity, students are challenged to think of C as an independent variable just like y, and D as a dependent variable just like x. If classroom discussion is lively, this kind of boundary-busting can really lead to some rich connections.

It is important that students take the opening part of the activity—Imagine and Predict—seriously. This gives them an investment in the activity and exercises a part of their mathematical thinking that often doesn't get used enough. The key thing here isn't right or wrong, it's the quality of the explanations. Teachers should use their intuition as to whether to provide hints during this section, as "getting the answer" may diminish some students' interest in the rest of the activity!

Construction Tips

Step 2: Students need to click first on the midpoint and second on one of the endpoints for the circle to be "attached" properly. The most common mistake students make is to click the second time in blank space in such a way that while the circle *appears* to pass through the endpoint, it's not *constructed* to do so if dragged.

Step 4: The desired commands won't be available if too many objects are selected. Always deselect all objects first by clicking in blank space.

The Circumference Function

Continued from previous page.

Q3: To see that the circumference really does equal pi, students may want to increase the precision of the circumference measurement. To do this, select the measurement and choose **Properties** from the Edit menu. On the Value panel, choose **hundred-thousandths** from the Precision pop-up menu.

Step 9: Students can use the **Ray** tool to construct the ray. (Press on the current **Straightedge** tool, then drag and release over the **Ray** tool in the palette of tools that appears.) Or they can select, in order, the origin and the plotted point and choose **Ray** from the Construct menu. To measure the ray's slope, select it and choose **Slope** from the Measure menu.

Sketch and Investigate

Q1 The trace is a ray, emanating from the origin. More details to come in subsequent answers!

Further Exploration

Q2 It makes sense because a circle with a diameter of 0 would have a circumference of 0. If students don't accept that a 0 diameter, 0 circumference circle exists, a limit argument might work: Basically, a circle with a really tiny diameter would have a really tiny circumference and as one approaches 0 so would the other.

That the trace goes through (or at least to!) the origin tells us that b is 0. This is because b represents a line's y-intercept.

Q3 The approximate circumference is 3.14 if Distance Precision is set to **hundredths**, 3.14159 if set to **hundred-thousandths**. This number is π (rounded).

Q4 The ratio stays the same—an approximation of π—no matter the size of the circle. (The one exception to this is if the endpoints are dragged right on top of each other, in which case the diameter becomes 0 and the ratio is undefined.)

Q5 It tells us that $m = \pi$ since m represents a line's slope.

Q6 $f(x) = \pi \cdot x$

Explore More

1. The appropriate domain is either $x > 0$ or $x \geq 0$. (This distinction could make for an interesting discussion!)

2. The plot will be a parabola. Specifically, it will be the parabola with the equation $y = \pi x^2$, which corresponds with the familiar area formula $A = \pi r^2$.

Functions in a Triangle (page 100)

Student Audience: Pre-algebra / Algebra 1

Prerequisites: Some basic familiarity with graphing in the x-y plane.

Sketchpad Proficiency: Intermediate

Activity Time: 25–35 minutes

Example Sketch: Triangle Functions.gsp from the folder **4_Functions**. The pages of this document show the activity as it's supposed to be after steps 5, 6, and 9.

General Notes: The key geometric relationship in this activity is that triangles DBE and ABC are similar. Thus, as D travels along segment AB, triangle DBE forms an infinite number of similar triangles. Since corresponding parts of similar triangles are proportional, the ratio of the length of $\overline{DE}$ to the distance from B to $\overline{DE}$ will always be the same. (This in turn will be the slope of the locus segment.)

Students who have taken high school geometry already should be able to understand and discuss this geometric relationship. Students without this background should also be able to understand it, albeit less formally.

Construction Tips

Step 2: Students need to make sure to click on existing endpoints of segments when drawing the second and third sides of the triangle. At the end of this step, students should have three segments and three points (labeled A, B, and C) in their sketches.

Step 3: Segment AB should highlight before you click. Try dragging the new point with the **Arrow** tool after this step to confirm that it can only move along the segment.

Step 5: An alternate way to construct the point of intersection is to select the line and the segment and choose **Intersection** from the Construct menu.

Step 6: To hide the line, select it and choose **Hide Line** from the Display menu. Use the **Segment** tool to construct segment DE, or select D and E and choose **Segment** from the Construct menu.

Investigate

Q1 Answers will vary. The important thing here is to take this step seriously. Perhaps students can be asked to defend their choices in writing or discuss them in groups.

Q2 The graph is a straight line—or, more specifically, a straight line segment—with one endpoint at the origin and the other somewhere in the first quadrant. The fact that the graph is linear shows that as one quantity changes at a steady rate, so does the other (though one may change faster than the other). The fact that it goes through (or at least to) the origin shows that when the distance between B and $\overline{DE}$ is 0, so is the length of $\overline{DE}$.

Q3 The domain is the set of distances from 0 to the height of $\triangle ABC$, inclusive. The smallest the distance can be, 0, occurs when D is at B. The greatest the distance can be, equal to the height of $\triangle ABC$, occurs when D is at A and $\overline{DE}$ coincides with $\overline{AC}$.

The range is the set of lengths from 0 to the length of $\overline{AC}$, inclusive. The smallest the length can be, 0, occurs when D is at B. The greatest the length can be, equal to the length of $\overline{AC}$, occurs when D is at A and $\overline{DE}$ coincides with $\overline{AC}$.

Q4 The larger the base is relative to the height (shorter, wider triangles), the steeper is the slope. This is because the length of $\overline{DE}$ changes very quickly for very small changes in the distance. The smaller the base is relative to the height (taller, skinnier triangles), the less steep the slope is. This is because, as the distance from B to $\overline{DE}$ changes a lot, the length of $\overline{DE}$ changes much more slowly.

Furthermore, a pair of similar triangles would produce graphs with the same slope. The only difference is that the larger triangle would have the larger domain and range.

Explore More

1. Since the slope of the segment is the ratio of the two measurements, the function to plot is: $f(x) = (m \, \overline{DE} / \text{Distance } B \text{ to } \overline{DE}) \cdot x$.

   To make the plot coincide exactly with the locus, change its domain on the Plot Properties panel. (Select the plot, choose **Properties** from the Edit menu, and click on the Plot tab.)

2. These plots will be similar to the original plot—segments from the origin—but with slopes less than or equal to that of the original plot. This is because the shortest distance from B to $\overline{DE}$ is along a perpendicular, and this is how the distance from B to $\overline{DE}$ is measured. Since the ratio corresponding to the slope of the plots has BD, BE, or the distance from B to $\overline{DE}$ in the denominator, the shortest distance corresponds to the greatest slope. The slopes would be equal for right triangles. (For example, if C were a right angle, the length of $\overline{BE}$ would equal the distance from B to $\overline{DE}$ and these two plots would coincide.)

3. Relationships between linear values (height, for example) and the area will be quadratic.

Functional Geometry (page 102)

Student Audience: Pre-algebra/Algebra 1

Prerequisites: Some basic familiarity with graphing in the x-y plane and functions. Note that the previous two activities serve as good introductions to this activity and, in fact, involve the same figures as on the first two pages of the multi-page document used in this activity.

Sketchpad Proficiency: Intermediate. Beginners will need some help with how to measure objects and would be well advised to start by doing either or both of the previous two activities. Students with more Sketchpad experience should be encouraged to add things to the constructions and measure less obvious quantities.

Activity Time: 25–50 minutes. This really depends on how much exploration students do. If they plot only the suggested functions listed in the table, they should be able to finish quickly. But if they explore their own functions, discuss what they find, and try to find and plot equations to match their findings, the activity will obviously take quite a bit longer (and be much more rewarding).

Required Sketch: Geometric Functions.gsp from the folder **4_Functions**

General Notes: Various forms of this activity have been used successfully for many years in workshops and classrooms. The key is having an atmosphere in which students feel comfortable exploring things on their own. If they do, they're sure to find many interesting functional relationships beyond those listed. There are even some quartic (4th degree) polynomials lurking for those curious enough to find them.

One important topic for classroom discussion is linear versus quadratic relationships. When do you expect to see a line and when do you expect to see a parabola? (In general, one expects to see a line when plotting lengths against other lengths—such as a side length and the perimeter of a figure—and a parabola when plotting a length against an area.)

Construction Tips

Step 5: Another way to see the plotted point if it isn't visible is to make the figure smaller. Students may also want to move the origin to a more convenient location and possibly hide the grid (by choosing **Hide Grid** from the Graph menu). To gain greater control over axis scaling, choose **Rectangular Grid** from the Graph | Grid Form submenu—you'll now be able to rescale each axis independently using its own unit point.

Representing Functions Dynamically: Introducing Dynagraphs (page 104)

Student Audience: Algebra 1/Algebra 2

Prerequisites: Students need to have already been introduced to functions to do this activity as written (although a teacher certainly could use the **Dynagraphs.gsp** sketch to introduce functions). The earlier activities in this chapter could serve as an effective introduction to functions, but it would probably be best to supplement these with other types of experiences with functions.

Sketchpad Proficiency: Beginner. Students manipulate a pre-made sketch.

Activity Time: 30–50 minutes. The time required depends on how seriously students take writing descriptions of the dynagraphs and on whether the Explore More section is attempted. To reduce the amount of time required, Q4 can be skipped.

Required Sketch: Dynagraphs.gsp from the folder **4_Functions**

General Notes: The term *dynagraph* was coined by Paul Goldenberg, Philip Lewis, and James O'Keefe in their study "Dynamic Representation and the Development of a Process Understanding of Functions" published by Education Development Center, Inc., and supported in part by a grant from the National Science Foundation.

The motivation for developing and using dynagraphs comes from the often-noted difficulty students have in seeing the graphs of functions not just as static pictures but as dynamic representations of functional relationships between two quantities. By "decoupling" the input and output axes and having an arrow connect points on either (as opposed to having the axes arranged perpendicularly with single points representing particular input-output dyads), students are better able to see the "input-output machine" view of functions expressed graphically. Being able to drag the input pointer gives students the further advantage of seeing functions as *dynamic* relationships between quantities.

Thus, dynagraphs can be thought of as a bridge between the "input-output machine" model with which students are often introduced to functions (epitomized by verbal or symbolic representations of functions) and function graphs in the Cartesian plane. This is the approach taken in this chapter.

Therefore, to use this activity (and the rest of the dynagraph activities) effectively, it's important to first make sure students understand that dynagraphs are representations of functions with all that that entails and, second, to connect dynagraphs to other representations of functions.

Sketch and Investigate

Q1 Answers will vary, but should basically describe functions as "consistent input-output machines." In other words, they are relations or mappings between input values and output values such that any valid input value maps to a single output value. There are obviously other acceptable ways of describing functions.

Q2 The dynagraphs do represent functions because, first, they map input values to output values and, second, they are consistent in that a particular input value will always point to the same output value.

Q3 Many possible answers. Good answers will in general include dynamic descriptions ("As the input is dragged steadily from left to right, the output . . .") and note any symmetries present.

Q4 See Q3.

Q5 $y = -1$ $b = 2$
$n = 7$ d is undefined
$x = -1$ $r = 9$
$? = -8$ $z = 1$
$p = -8$ $s = 3$
$m = \ldots -7, -3, 1, 5, \ldots$ $a = 2.5$

Explore More

1. Function u has an absolute maximum of 8 at $(\ldots -7, -3, 1, 5, \ldots)$.
    Function i has an absolute minimum of 0 at 0.
    Function v has an absolute minimum of 0 at 0.
    Function u has an absolute minimum of -8 at $(\ldots -5, -1, 3, 7, \ldots)$.

From Dynagraphs to Cartesian Graphs (page 107)

Student Audience: Algebra 1/Algebra 2

Prerequisites: Student should already have been introduced to dynagraphs by doing the previous activity.

Sketchpad Proficiency: Beginner. Students manipulate a pre-made sketch and add on to it minimally.

Activity Time: 40–50 minutes

Required Sketch: DynaToCart.gsp from the folder **4_Functions**

General Notes: See the previous activity's Activity Notes for a more thorough discussion of dynagraphs in general.

The purpose of this activity is to illuminate the dynamic nature of Cartesian graphs by showing how they can be created from dynagraphs. In the notes to the previous activity, we stated:

> The motivation for developing and using dynagraphs comes from the often-noted difficulty students have in seeing the graphs of functions not just as static pictures but as dynamic representations of functional relationships between two quantities.

Nowhere is that more true than in this activity. By seeing a dynagraph "morph" into a Cartesian graph—then being able to treat the result both as a dynagraph and as a Cartesian graph—students viscerally experience the dynamic nature of Cartesian graphs. Granted, it's a lot to ask Algebra 1 students to "wrap their minds" around all that this entails (and, beyond that, to articulate it in writing or orally), but we believe that the very experience of playing with these sketches and playing with these ideas is valuable in itself.

Thus, any discussion of the relationships between the two types of functional representations, any further attempt to make sense of what's going on in this activity, should be beneficial even if (especially if?) students are left feeling that they don't yet totally "get it."

From Dynagraphs to Cartesian Graphs

Continued from previous page.

A good way to explore the behavior of these functions is with animation. Once you've entered an equation on page 3, drag the input pointer to the left of the screen. Then select the input pointer (or point *A*) and choose **Animate Pentagon** (or **Animate Point**) from the Display menu (or click the Animate button on the Motion Controller). The input pointer will animate at a steady pace from left to right, allowing you to focus on the functional behavior rather than dragging. (If the pointer animates from right to left, just press the Reverse Direction button on the Motion Controller.)

Construction Tips

Step 4: Students can certainly construct the perpendiculars on their own instead of pressing the button. Simply select point *A* and the input axis and choose **Perpendicular Line** from the Construct menu to construct one of the lines; do the same with point *f(A)* and the output axis to construct the other.

Step 5: An alternate way to construct the point of intersection is to select the two lines and choose **Intersection** from the Construct menu.

Step 7: An alternative to tracing in (or a good follow-up) is to construct the locus of the intersection point as the input pointer varies along its axis. To do this, select the intersection point and point *A*, then choose **Locus** from the Construct menu. This is an especially good thing to do if you plan on changing the function equation for this dynagraph.

Function Matchmaking

Q1 a. 4
    b. 2
    c. 5
    d. 1
    e. 3

From Dynagraphs to Cartesian Graphs

Q2 Many possible answers. Two things that change are the length and orientation of the segment connecting the two dynagraph points. Neither of these changes (nor any other) is mathematically significant in terms of what dynagraphs represent. Everything having to do with the functional relationship itself stays the same as the output axis is tilted. Specifically, if $f(a) = b$ before tilting, $f(a) = b$ after tilting.

Q3 The x-coordinate of the new point is the same as the value of *A*—the input of the dynagraph. Similarly, the y-coordinate of the new point is the same as the value of $f(A)$—the input of the dynagraph. This makes sense since in the x-y plane, points lying along vertical lines have the same x-coordinates while those along horizontal lines have the same y-coordinates.

Q4 The graph is a line with positive slope. The fact that it's a line corresponds to the fact that as the input pointer on the dynagraph is dragged at a constant speed, the output pointer moves at a constant speed. How far the input pointer goes in a given unit of time corresponds to *run,* and how far the output pointer goes corresponds to *rise.* The fact that the line has a positive slope corresponds to the fact that the two pointers always go the same direction (see Q6). The fact that the slope of the line is greater than 1 corresponds to the fact that the output pointer moves faster than the input pointer. (A slope of 1 would correspond to pointers moving the same speed; a slope of between 0 and 1 would correspond to a slower output pointer.)

Simultaneous Representation

Q5 A Cartesian point contains two pieces of information—its x-coordinate and its y-coordinate. As we saw in Q3, the x-coordinate corresponds to the value of the input pointer (or point) and the y-coordinate corresponds to the value of the output pointer (or point). Thus, a Cartesian point, by virtue of its representing a *coordinate pair*, contains both the input and output values of a particular dynagraph position.

Q6 When the input and output pointers both move right, the Cartesian point moves *up*.

When the input pointer moves right and the output pointer moves left, the Cartesian point moves *down*.

Q7 The Cartesian graph of $f(x) = 5x$ is *steeper* than that of $f(x) = x$. This corresponds to the fact that the output pointer moves faster for the dynagraph of $f(x) = 5x$ than it does for that of $f(x) = x$. (See Q4 for a more detailed answer.)

Q8 Many possible answers.

Exploring Domain and Range with Dynagraphs and Cartesian Graphs (page 110)

Student Audience: Algebra 1/Algebra 2

Prerequisites: Students should already have been introduced to dynagraphs by doing the previous two activities. Note that for most students, some previous introduction to domain and range is probably necessary, as this activity covers quite a lot for a first experience with this challenging topic.

Sketchpad Proficiency: Beginner. Students manipulate a pre-made sketch and add on to it only minimally.

Activity Time: 30–40 minutes

Required Sketch: Domain Range.gsp from the folder 4_Functions

General Notes: See the Activity Notes from Representing Functions Dynamically—Introducing Dynagraphs for a more thorough discussion of dynagraphs in general.

A good discussion topic before starting this activity might focus on why, in some functions, some numbers might not be allowed as inputs. Can students think of functions with restricted domains? One category of answers to this question is covered in the activity—namely, functions such as square root functions and rational functions that have undefined outputs for certain inputs. A category not covered, though, is functions modeling real-life or geometric situations. For example, the function $f(x) = 2.50x$ might represent the total cost of buying x magazines each costing $2.50. But it wouldn't make sense to consider $x = -2$ or $x = 3.71$ here—only whole numbers are part of this domain.

Another good discussion topic might be the limitations of technology. "What are some situations in which technology might mislead you when doing math?" One such situation would be not taking into account the fact that calculators *round* infinite decimals. By using a result such as 0.66666667 (instead of 2/3) in further calculations on a certain problem, error can creep in. The point is not, of course, that the calculator is inadequate in this situation, just that one needs to be aware of what the calculator can and can't do.

Throughout this activity, a good way to go beyond what's written is to encourage students to edit the various functions and observe the results. (To edit a function, double-click its equation and make the appropriate changes in the Edit Function dialog box

that appears.) After step 2, for example, you could ask students how the range would change if they changed the function to $f(x) = \text{round}(x) + 1$ (*answer:* it wouldn't). You could then ask for what values of k would the function $f(x) = \text{round}(x) + k$ have a different range than that of the original function (*answer:* non-integer values). You could follow this up by exploring what happens when you multiply round(x) by a constant. You could expand on the activity in similar ways after Q1, Q4, Q5, and step 6.

By the way, the reason that the "round" function has its own page for Cartesian representation (page 5) is that it needs to be plotted "discretely" instead of "continuously." In other words, it needs to be plotted as a set of "dots" instead of as a set of dots connected by segments. This is because it's a step function and thus has discontinuities. If it were plotted continuously, the discontinuities would be connected with segments (making it look like true steps, actually!) To change whether a plot—or a locus—is plotted continuously or discretely, go to that object's Plot Properties panel. To do that, select the object, choose **Properties** from the Edit menu, and click on the Plot tab.

Sketch and Investigate

Q1 $g(x)$: all real numbers

   $h(x)$: $i(x) \geq 0$

   $i(x)$: all real numbers

   $j(x)$: $-2 \leq u(x) \leq 2$

Q2 The range appears to be all integers, as with $f(x) = \text{round}(x)$. This is clearly wrong since many (most!) non-integer inputs will result in non-integer outputs. For example, $g(0.01) = 0.2$.

The reason that the output pointer only lands on integers in the dynagraph is that the input pointer can't be dragged continuously—it gets dragged one pixel (screen unit) at a time and this dynagraph was set up so that each pixel is worth 0.05 (1/20) units. This can easily be changed by pressing the *Show Unit Points* button and changing the scale of the input axis.

The reason that animating slowly (as students are encouraged to do in the next step) may work better is that the animating object can be slowed down to such an extent that it "moves" less than one pixel per unit time—less than can be achieved by dragging. Such minute changes may not be discernable on screen due to the limitations of screen resolution, but will be reflected in the calculation that determines the location of the output pointer.

Exploring Domain and Range with Dynagraphs and Cartesian Graphs

Continued from previous page.

Q3 The domain of function v is $x \geq 0$. (When the input point is at $x < 0$, the output pointer disappears.)

The range of function v is $v(x) \geq 0$.

Q4 The reason is that the square root of any negative number is undefined over the set of real numbers.

Q5 The only domain restriction for w is 2, and the only number not in its range is 0. (In other words, the domain is: all real numbers, $x \neq 2$; the range is: all real numbers, $f(x) \neq 0$.)

The reason that 2 is excluded from the domain is that that would result in division by 0, which is undefined. The reason that 0 isn't part of the range is that no matter what the value of the denominator of $1/(x-2)$ is, the result can't be 0.

Domain and Range on Cartesian Graphs

Q6 Here's one way to determine domain and range by looking at a Cartesian graph of a function: Imagine a vertical line perpendicular to the x-axis that sweeps from left to right or right to left. Any location where the line touches the graph is part of the domain. Thus, if a vertical line crossing the x-axis at $x = 3$ touches the graph somewhere, 3 is part of the domain of that function. Any location where the line doesn't touch the graph at all, up or down or even on the x-axis itself, is not part of the domain.

Similarly, to determine the range from a Cartesian graph, imagine a horizontal line perpendicular to the y-axis sweeping up to down or down to up. Anywhere it touches some part of the graph is part of the range; anywhere it doesn't, isn't.

Explore More

1. To make f's range all even numbers, use $f(x) = 2 \cdot \text{round}(x)$.

   To make f's range all odd numbers, use $f(x) = 2 \cdot \text{round}(x) + 1$.

   To make v's domain and range all numbers less than or equal to 0, use $v(x) = -\sqrt{-x}$.

   To make w's domain all real numbers except 0 and its range all real numbers except 2, use

   $$w(x) = \frac{1}{x} + 2.$$

Exploring Odd and Even Functions with Dynagraphs and Cartesian Graphs (page 113)

Student Audience: Algebra 1 / Algebra 2

Prerequisites: Students should already have been introduced to dynagraphs by doing at least the first two dynagraph activities: Representing Functions Dynamically—Introducing Dynagraphs and From Dynagraphs to Cartesian Graphs. Note that for most students, some previous introduction to odd and even functions is probably necessary, as this activity covers quite a lot for a first experience with this challenging topic.

Sketchpad Proficiency: Beginner. Students manipulate a pre-made sketch and add on to it minimally.

Activity Time: 30–40 minutes

Required Sketch: Odd Even.gsp from the folder **4_Functions**

General Notes: See the Activity Notes from Representing Functions Dynamically—Introducing Dynagraphs for a more thorough discussion of dynagraphs in general.

Before introducing odd and even functions, you may wish to tell students that one thing mathematicians often do is classify mathematical objects based on properties that make them unusual or special. For example, even numbers are special because they're always divisible by 2; prime numbers are special because they have no proper divisors. What types of properties might functions have that would be unusual or special? Students have already seen some: the round(x) function is unusual because of the many breaks it contains—it can't be drawn without lifting your pencil. Functions sharing that property are called discontinuous. This kind of discussion will set the stage for the investigation of odd and even functions.

One important thing to keep in mind when doing this activity is the difference between "negative" and "opposite." For example, in the equation $f(-x) = -f(x)$ that characterizes odd functions, the input on the left side of the equation isn't necessarily negative—it's just the opposite of the input on the right side. Similarly, the output on the right side isn't necessarily negative—it's just the opposite of the output on the left side. It's important to make sure students understand this point.

Sketch and investigate

Q1 They are opposites. For example, $f(2) = 4$ and $f(-2) = -4$.

Q2 The functions $g(x)$ and $i(x)$ are also odd. The function $h(x)$ is neither odd nor even.

Q3 They are the same. For example, $t(3) = 7$ and $t(-3) = -7$.

Q4 The functions $u(x)$ and $v(x)$ are also even. The function $w(x)$ is neither even nor odd.

Q5 If it's odd, its behavior on the right side of the origin will "mirror" its behavior on the left side of the origin. If it's even, an input to the right of the origin will point to the same spot as an input the same distance to the left of the origin.

Q6 Odd functions are symmetrical about the origin, meaning that if they are spun 180° about the origin, they'll wind up looking the same. Even functions are symmetrical across the y-axis, meaning that folding the graph along the y-axis would cause the two halves of the graph to sit right on top of each other.

Q7 The functions $f(x) = 5x$, $f(x) = x^3 - 2x$, and $f(x) = \sin(x)$ are all odd.

The functions $f(x) = x^2 + 2$ and $f(x) = \cos(x)$ are both even.

The function $f(x) = x^4 - 3x^3$ is neither.

Explore More

1. An easy way to tell if a polynomial is odd or even is to look at the degrees of its terms (meaning the values of the powers of x). If they're all odd, it's an odd function. This is why odd functions are called "odd." If the degrees are all even, it's an even function. This is why even functions are called "even." Constants (such as the 2 in $f(x) = x^2 + 2$) are considered even-degreed terms since they can be thought of as being a constant times x^0 (for example, $2 = 2x^0$).

2. If $f(x)$ and $g(x)$ are both odd, $(f + g)(x)$ is also odd. One way to see this would be to redefine $h(x)$ on page 1 of **Odd Even.gsp** as $f(x) + g(x)$ and then explore the resulting dynagraph. Another way is as follows: $(f + g)(-x)$ $= f(-x) + g(-x) = -f(x) + -g(x) = -[f(x) + g(x)]$ $= -(f + g)(x)$. Look at the first and last expressions to see that $(f + g)(x)$ is indeed odd.

Using one of these methods, you can see that if $f(x)$ and $g(x)$ are both odd, $(f \cdot g)(x)$ is also odd.

Exploring Function Composition with Dynagraphs (page 115)

Student Audience: Algebra 1 / Algebra 2

Prerequisites: Students should already have been introduced to dynagraphs by doing at least the first two dynagraph activities: Representing Functions Dynamically—Introducing Dynagraphs and From Dynagraphs to Cartesian Graphs. Note that for all but the brightest students, some previous introduction to composite functions is probably necessary, as this activity perhaps covers too much too quickly for a first experience with this challenging topic.

Sketchpad Proficiency: Beginner. Students manipulate a pre-made sketch and add on to it minimally.

Activity Time: 35–45 minutes

Required Sketch: Composition.gsp from the folder **4_Functions**

General Notes: See the Activity Notes from Representing Functions Dynamically—Introducing Dynagraphs for a more thorough discussion of dynagraphs in general.

An important thing to be aware of is that composite dynagraphs often seem "backwards" to students. Since one reads $g(f(x))$ left to right, one may be surprised to see that its composite dynagraph starts at f's input pointer and ends at g's output pointer. The reason, of course, is that when evaluating $g(f(x))$, you start on the *inside* by evaluating $f(x)$ and go from there. Make sure students really do understand why composite dynagraphs are structured as they are.

A possible discussion topic with students is the fact that function composition lurks behind *every* function. For example, the simple function $f(x) = 2x + 1$ can be seen as $g(h(x))$, where $g(x) = x + 1$ and $h(x) = 2x$, or $g(x) = 2x$ and $h(x) = x + 0.5$, or $g(x) = 2x + 1$ and $h(x) = x$, or many other possibilities. Students may enjoy "decomposing" functions in this way.

Note that the only way to undo merging an input point with an output point is literally to undo—that it, use the **Undo** command from the Edit menu repeatedly (or hold down the Shift key and choose **Undo All**). Splitting (with the **Split** command) won't work because the original output points weren't constructed as points on objects or one of the other types of splittable points.

Exploring Function Composition with Dynagraphs

Continued from previous page.

Introduction

Q1 a. 100   b. 18   c. 8
     d. 18   e. 17   f. 17

Q2 No, $f(g(x))$ doesn't always equal $g(f(x))$. In this case, $f(g(5)) = 50$ and $g(f(5)) = 100$.

Sketch and Investigate

Q3 a. 2   b. 2   c. 98

Q4 The range of $g(h(x))$ is all squares of whole numbers, or, (0, 1, 4, 9, 16, 25, 36, . . .).

A nice way to see this is to trace the output pointer (by selecting it and choosing **Trace Triangle** from the Display menu) and then drag the input pointer. This is, in fact, the method used in Exploring Domain and Range with Dynagraphs and Cartesian graphs.

Q5 The output is always the same as the input in both cases. This is because $f(x)$ and $i(x)$ are inverse functions of each other, meaning that they "undo" each other. In other words, start with any number, double it, then halve it, and you'll end up where you started. It works the same if you halve it first, then double it.

Explore More

1.   a. $f(g(h(x)))$
     b. $g(f(h(x)))$
     c. $g(i(h(x)))$

Thinking Differently: Again and Again (page 117)

Student Audience: Algebra 1/Algebra 2

Prerequisites: Students should be familiar with the concept of slope, and have at least some basic introduction to functions.

Sketchpad Proficiency: Beginner/Intermediate. Students learn how to use Sketchpad's iteration functionality.

Activity Time: 30–40 minutes.

Example Sketch: AgainAndAgain.gsp from the folder **4_Functions**. The pages of this document show the activity as it's supposed to be after step 5, step 7, Q4, step 8, and Q6.

General Notes: This activity probes and strengthens students' understanding of slope by approaching it from the novel perspective of iterated relationships. Iterative thinking pervades mathematics—from the simple act of counting to the analysis of dynamical systems—and the notation students encounter here may reappear as *difference equations* later in their mathematical careers. The Explore More section pursues the idea of iteration beyond the realm of linear relationships.

Encourage students to take the opening part of the activity—Imagine and Predict—seriously. Having their working hypotheses confirmed or denied by experimental evidence offers students an opportunity to reflect on their own understanding, something they may miss if they move forward too quickly.

In this activity, students may describe a set of iterated points as *being* a line, or as having a linear relationship. Consider discussing whether a line can be made up of 6 or 7 points or, if points themselves can be linearly related. Students might also be encouraged to explain how they know that the points form a line—leading to further discussions about the role of slope.

In Q3 through Q5, students are asked to determine the slope of the line passing through the iterated points. Students can be encouraged to test their answers by constructing a ray from point *A* through their new point and measuring the slope of that ray. Consider asking whether a line or ray is more appropriate and why.

In Q6, students are encouraged to come up with other linear equations both in order to de-mystify the specific one chosen in the question—there's nothing special about $y = 3x + 2$—and in order to reflect on whether some equations are 'trickier' to match than others.

There are many other variations of the iteration rules that students can explore. Encourage them to identify others that yield interesting results. Alternatively, can you 'move backwards' from a graph to an iteration rule? For example, is it possible to find an iteration rule that will produce a given parabola?

A crucial idea that emerges from the Explore More portion of this activity is the importance of notation. A succinct and powerful notation is introduced here, but teachers who wish to pursue iterative applications may wish to introduce this notation even earlier in the activity. Alternately, students could be encouraged to develop their own notation systems for describing iteration rules. For instance, another way of describing the iteration rule $(x_{new}, y_{new}) = (x_{old} + 1, 2 \cdot y_{old})$ is to write $x \rightarrow x + 1$ and $y \rightarrow 2 \cdot y$.

Construction Tips

Step 2: After measuring the point's abscissa, students will have to click in blank space (or hit the Esc key) to deselect the new measurement, then reselect the point and measure its ordinate.

Step 6: Students may need to drag the dialog box in order to see the point on which to click.

Q4–Q6: When students are asked to change or edit a calculation they've made earlier, they can select the calculation and choose **Edit Calculation** from the Edit menu, or just double-click it.

Sketch and Investigate

Q1 The sequence of iterated images are a set of points which lay on a ray or line.

Q2 The values change according to the location of point A. Specifically, each row represents the coordinates of a point in the sequence, with the first row ($n = 0$) referring to point A's first image point. Even though the values all change as A is dragged, the values row to row always increase by one, which explains why the digits to the right of the decimal places are always the same down each row.

Q3 The slope of the line is 1.

Q4 When the rule is changed to $(y_A + 4)$, the slope is 4 and the values in the right column increase by 4 from one row to the next. When the rule changes to $(y_A - 3)$, the slope is -3 and the values in the right column decrease by 3 from one row to the next. In general when the rules are $(x_A + 1)$ and $(y_A + k)$, the value of the slope will be k.

Q5 The slope in Q2 is 1. The slope of the imaginary line produced by the rules $(x_A + n)$ and $(y_A + m)$ is m/n. Therefore when $m = n$, the slope will equal 1.

Q6 Answers may vary. One way to attack this problem is to focus first on the slope of the equation $y = 3x + 2$. In order to obtain a slope of 3, the iteration rules $(x_A + n)$ and $(y_A + m)$ must have $m/n = 3$, or $m = 3n$. In order to match the y-intercept of the equation (which is 2), it is sufficient to move the starting point to the point $(0, 2)$. Therefore, one solution is to use the iteration rules $(x_A + 1)$ and $(y_A + 3)$ and a starting point of $(0, 2)$. More generally, the iteration rules $(x_A + k)$ and $(y_A + 3k)$ will yield the required slope while the starting point can be anywhere along the line $y = 3x + 2$.

Explore More

1. Repeated multiplication by 2 doubles values on each iteration, producing an exponential curve. For example, starting at $y_{old} = 1$ produces the sequences of powers of 2. That is, the imaginary curve through the points generated by the iteration rule $(x_{new}, y_{new}) = (x_{old} + 1, 2 \cdot y_{old})$ can be expressed as $y = 2^x$, assuming a starting position of $(0, 1)$. In general, the imaginary curve through the points generated by the iteration rule $(x_{new}, y_{new}) = (x_{old} + 1, k \cdot y_{old})$ will be $y = k^x$. It might be interesting to identify the form of the exponential equation for different starting positions.

2. The new iteration forms two parallel lines which have a reflection symmetry around the line $y = x$. Try joining the starting point with the plotted point before iterating to produce a zig-zag pattern, which brings out the reflection symmetry. Students might also try variations of this inverse iteration rule similar to the variations performed on the original iteration rule.

Translation in the
Coordinate Plane (page 125)

Student Audience: Pre-algebra/Algebra 1

Prerequisites: Students should understand the (x, y) notation of a point in the coordinate plane. Some previous familiarity with translations is also helpful. The term *translation vector* is used and defined. The term *image* (as in "the coordinates of its image under a translation") is used but not defined, so a teacher may want to discuss this terminology from transformational geometry.

Sketchpad Proficiency: Intermediate. Students start with a blank sketch and construct everything from scratch. All steps are clearly explained (and extra tips are given below), but if a student is unfamiliar with Sketchpad it might take longer.

Activity Time: 35–45 minutes. If you have less time or are working with inexperienced Sketchpad users, you can use the sketch **Translate.gsp**. Have students open this sketch, drag points *A–D* around to familiarize themselves with the setup, then start the activity at step 8.

Example Sketch: Translate.gsp from the folder 5_Tranform. The pages of this document show the activity as it's supposed to be after steps 4 and 9.

General Notes: Teachers may wish to begin this activity by discussing vectors. What are vectors? How are they different from lines, rays, or segments?

If students find this activity too easy, teachers may suggest they try translating several times with the same vector, or translating using two or more different vectors. How are the final images related to the translation vectors in each case? Students may also try using vectors whose tails aren't attached to the origin.

Another possible discussion topic is whether there are other ways of defining a translation vector besides specifying two points (its tail and head). One way is to specify a distance and an angle (called a *polar vector*); another way is to specify a horizontal distance and a vertical distance (called a *rectangular vector*). Any of these three methods of specifying a vector can be used in Sketchpad, although the focus of this discussion need not be on Sketchpad functionality *per se*. Which of these three methods is easiest?

The definition in the first paragraph of the activity is from Webster's New World Dictionary of Mathematics (1989).

Construction Tips

The instructions assume that the Text panel of Preferences retains the default settings, with For All New Points unchecked, and As Objects Are Measured checked. If your settings are different, you can either change them in Text Preferences (choose **Preferences** from the Edit menu) or use the **Text** tool to label points manually.

Steps 2 and 5: Click *near* a grid point to have the point constructed *at* the grid point. If you click too far away from a grid point, the point will be constructed right at the spot of the click and you'll then need to drag the point to get it to a grid point.

Step 8: The easiest way to select the entire triangle (assuming it's all in one quadrant) is by using a selection marquee.

Sketch and Investigate

Q1 If you drag point D along the x-axis, the y-coordinates of a vertex and its image point will be equal. If you drag point D along the y-axis, the x-coordinates of a vertex and its image point will be equal.

Q2 If the vector translates the triangle to the left and up, point C is in the second quadrant. Its x-coordinate is negative (causing the leftward movement) and its y-coordinate is positive (causing the upward movement).

Q3 The image of (x, y) under a translation by (s, t) is the point $(x + s, y + t)$. Note that this answer holds regardless of the signs of $x, y, s,$ or t.

If this question is difficult for students, have them generate actual values for $x, y, s,$ and t—all positive at first—and have them look for patterns.

Q4 Point M' will be at $(4, 1)$.

The reason is that the translation vector here is $(3, -1)$—three to the right and one down—and $(1 + 3, 2 + (-1)) = (4, 1)$.

Q5 Point D is at $(3, -1)$.

Explore More

1. All of the measurements are preserved except for the points' coordinates.

2. XYZ couldn't be the image of UVW under a translation because the three translation vectors aren't the same. The vectors used to get from U to X and V to Y are both $(-2, -2)$ whereas the vector used to get from W to Z is $(-1, -3)$. Other arguments are possible (for example, the two triangles aren't similar).

Rotation in the Coordinate Plane (page 127)

Student Audience: Pre-algebra/Algebra 1

Prerequisites: Students should understand the (x, y) notation of a point in the coordinate plane. Some previous familiarity with rotation is also helpful. The term *image* (as in "the coordinates of its image point after a 90° rotation") is used but not defined, so a teacher may want to discuss this terminology from transformational geometry.

Sketchpad Proficiency: Intermediate. Students start with a blank sketch and construct everything from scratch. All steps are clearly explained (and extra tips are given below), but if a student is unfamiliar with Sketchpad, it might take longer.

Activity Time: 30–40 minutes. If you have less time or are working with inexperienced Sketchpad users, you can use the sketch **Rotate.gsp** from the folder **5_Tranform**. Have students open this sketch, drag points A–D around to familiarize themselves with the set-up, then start the activity at step 6.

Example Sketch: **Rotate.gsp** from the folder **5_Transform**. The pages of this document show the activity as it's supposed to be after steps 4, 6, and 8.

General Notes: While this activity is progressing, teachers may wish to ask students why only multiples of 90° are being considered. This issue is addressed later in Explore More 3, but students may not get that far and it's worth thinking about before then anyway.

A good extension to this activity might involve asking students why the relationships in this activity hold. Students with prior experience with geometry would have an advantage here, but all students can explore the question fruitfully. Consider suggesting that students form the triangles defined by the origin, a point, and the point's image.

Another extension could be to discuss whether these relationships would hold if the center of rotation were other than the origin.

Construction Tips

The instructions assume that the Text panel of Preferences retains the default settings, with For All New Points unchecked, and As Objects Are Measured checked. If your settings are different, you can either change them in Text Preferences (choose **Preferences** from the Edit menu) or use the **Text** tool to label points manually.

Step 2: Click *near* a grid point to have the point constructed *at* the grid point. If you click too far away from a grid point, the point will be constructed right at the spot of the click and you'll then need to drag the point to get it to a grid point.

Steps 6 and 7: The easiest way to select the entire quadrilateral (assuming it's all in one quadrant) is by using a selection marquee.

Sketch and Investigate

Q1 If you switch the x- and y-coordinates of the original point, then change the sign of the new x-coordinate, you get the coordinates of the image point after a 90° rotation about the origin.

Q2 The coordinates of the image point are $(-b, a)$.

Q3 Both the x- and y-coordinates of the image point are the opposite of those of the original point.

The coordinates of the image of point (a, b) are $(-a, -b)$.

Q4 The coordinates of the image point are $(b, -a)$.

Explore More

1. Length, perimeter, and area are preserved. Coordinates and slope are not.

2. Imagine a segment connecting the origin and the point in question. The polar coordinates of the point are (r, θ) where r is the length of the segment and θ is the angle, measured counterclockwise, from the positive x-axis to the segment.

3. In a square coordinate system, it's difficult to see the relationship between the coordinates of a point and those of its image under a 45° rotation. In a polar coordinate system, the relationship is simple: The r-coordinates are the same and the θ-coordinate of the image point is that of the original point plus 45° (or minus 315°, depending on the original point's location).

Reflection in Geometry and Algebra (page 129)

Student Audience: Algebra 1

Prerequisites: Familiarity with the Cartesian plane

Sketchpad Proficiency: Beginner/Intermediate

Activity Time: 30–40 minutes

Example Sketch: Reflect.gsp from the folder 5_Transform. The pages of this document show the activity after steps 6, 10, 13, and 16. We recommend that you *not* try to shorten the activity by having students start at one of these junctures as the process of doing the actual geometric work is key to understanding the later algebraic process.

General Notes: This activity works well as a brush-up for students having problems with the coordinate plane, as an introduction to using Sketchpad for both geometry and algebra, and as a preparation for function transformation in the subsequent activity.

Before starting this activity, it would be good to brainstorm what students already know about reflection. A useful question to discuss—anticipating questions 4 and 6—is "If you stand 3 ft. from a mirror, how far do you *appear* to be from your reflected image?"

During the activity, you may wish to encourage students to continually connect the geometric and algebraic realms. For example, how do the relationships found in Q4 and Q6 relate to those from Q2?

If your class has done this and the previous two activities, you may want to end this activity by comparing all three transformations—translation, rotation, and reflection. Which transformation was the easiest to understand from an algebraic perspective? Which was the most surprising?

Construction Tips

Step 4: You may choose instead to leave Fade Traces Over Time unchecked so that traces remain on screen to be examined. In this case, students would periodically need to choose **Erase Traces** from the Display menu to clear traces from their screens.

Step 14: The reason for using **Coordinate Distance** instead of **Length** or **Distance** from the Measure menu is that students may have rescaled their axes at some point (so that coordinate units are different than the distance units of centimeters or inches). If students haven't touched the unit point, any of the three commands would work here as well.

Sketch and Investigate

Q1 Dragging a reflecting point results in a "mirror" pattern with the two traces mirroring each other across the line. Dragging a line point causes the reflected image point to draw a circle around the other line point. (The radius of this circle is the distance between the other line point and the reflecting pre-image.)

Q2 The line is the segment's *perpendicular bisector*, meaning that the angle they form is 90° and the line cuts the segment in half.

Q3 $(-a, b)$

Q4 $2a$ may be considered an acceptable answer; a more technically correct answer is $|2a|$ or $2|a|$. The absolute value signs ensure that the answer will be positive even if a is negative. This is desirable because the distance between two things is always considered to be positive (or 0).

Q5 $(c, -d)$

Q6 $2d$, $|2d|$, or $2|d|$ (See the answer to Q4 above.)

Explore More

1. The coordinates switch places. In other words, the image of a point (a, b) reflected across the line $y = x$ is the point (b, a).

2. These three transformations are equivalent. The coordinates of (a, b) after any of the transformations is $(-a, -b)$.

Reflecting Function Plots (page 132)

Student Audience: Algebra 1/Algebra 2

Prerequisites: This activity builds upon the previous one, but some students may be able to treat this as a stand-alone. Students need to have a pretty good understanding of functional notation and function plotting (graphing parabolas, for example).

Sketchpad Proficiency: Intermediate

Activity Time: 15–30 minutes

Example Sketch: Reflect Plot.gsp from the folder **5_Tranform**. The pages of this document show the activity as it's supposed to be after steps 2 and 5.

General Notes: A key to this activity is for students to understand the notation $y = f(x)$. Specifically, they need to understand that the part inside the parentheses refers to the input, the x, and altering it affects the horizontal aspect of the graph. The entire expression $f(x)$ refers to the input, the y, and altering it affects the vertical aspect of the graph. To a certain extent, that is what they are learning in the activity, but they'll have a hard time understanding this at all if they don't start out with a decent understanding of the notation.

Sketch and Investigate

Q1 The graphs of $y = f(x)$ and $y = -f(x)$ are reflections of each other across the x-axis.

The graphs of $y = f(x)$ and $y = f(-x)$ are reflections of each other across the y-axis.

Q2 The original graph is represented by the equation $y = f(x)$. In this equation, x refers to the x-coordinate (of course), and $f(x)$ refers to the y-coordinate (since y *equals* $f(x)$). Reflecting a point across the x-axis makes its y-coordinate the opposite of what it was, so it makes sense that the y-coordinates of *all* points on $y = -f(x)$ would be the opposite of those on $y = f(x)$. Similarly, reflecting a point across the y-axis makes its x-coordinate the opposite of what it was, so it makes sense that the x-coordinates of *all* points on $y = f(-x)$ would be the opposite of those on $y = f(x)$.

Explore More

1. The function $y = -f(-x)$ does the trick. The negative sign outside of $f(x)$ reflects f across the x-axis, and the one on the inside reflects it across the y-axis, as explained in the previous answer.

2. The functions $f(x) = x^2 + 3$ and $f(x) = x^6 + 3x^4 - 2x^2$ are both even; $f(x) = x^3$ and $f(x) = x^5 + 3x^3 - 8x$ are both odd; $f(x) = x^3 + 3$ is neither.

Reflecting Without the Reflect Command: The Algebra of Reflection (page 134)

Student Audience: Algebra 1/Algebra 2

Prerequisites: Doing the previous activity helps, but isn't necessary. Students do need very strong algebra skills to do this activity. The ability to find a line given a point and a perpendicular line, and the ability to solve simultaneous equations are both required. To simplify the activity, teachers may want to lead students through Q1–Q4, then have them do Q5 (and perhaps similar questions with C at different locations) on their own, following the model.

Sketchpad Proficiency: Intermediate

Activity Time: 40–50 minutes

Example Sketch: Reflect Algebra.gsp from the folder 5_Tranform. The pages of this document show the activity as it's supposed to be after steps 6 and 9. We recommend that you use these pages for reference and *not* try to shorten the activity by having students start at one of these junctures as the process of doing the actual geometric work is key to understanding the later algebraic process.

General Notes: This is a very challenging activity, but it's not beyond the abilities of strong Algebra 1 students. To make things a little easier, teachers might set up "Reflection Teams" of four students each. One student could find the equation of line AB, the second could find the equation of the line perpendicular to line AB through point C, the third could find the coordinates of point D, and the fourth could find the coordinates of point D'. Teams could do a few examples, then switch roles.

Construction Tips

Step 2: If students do things out of order, for example constructing a point *then* a line, point labels will contradict the many references in the activity. If this happens, students can either relabel the points using the **Text** tool (double-click on the label itself) or open a new sketch and start over.

An Algebraic Approach

Q1 $y = 2x$

Q2 $y = -0.5(x - 4) + 3$, or $y = -0.5x + 5$

The slope is -0.5 because that's the negative reciprocal of 2 $(-0.5 \cdot 2 = -1)$.

Q3 $(2, 4)$

Reflecting Without the Reflect Command: The Algebra of Reflection

Continued from previous page.

Q4 $(0, 5)$

The translation from C to D was left 2 and up 1, or $\langle -2, 1\rangle$. Translating D by this vector gives $(2 + (-2), 4 + 1) \Rightarrow (0, 5)$.

Q5 The equation of line CD will be $y = -0.5(x - 7) - 1$ or $y = -0.5x + 2.5$. The coordinates of point D will be $(1, 2)$. The translation vector from C to D will be $\langle -6, 3\rangle$. Point D' will be at $(-5, 5)$.

Explore More

1. The equation of line CD will be $y = -0.5(x - a) + b$, or $y = -0.5x + (0.5a + b)$. The coordinates of point D will be $(0.2a + 0.4b, 0.4a + 0.8b)$. The translation vector from C to D will be $\langle -0.8a + 0.4b, 0.4a - 0.2b\rangle$. And point D' will be at $(-0.6a + 0.8b, 0.8a + 0.6b)$.

   To check, plug in $a = 4$ and $b = 3$ and see if your answers are the same as in Q2–Q4, or plug in $a = 7$ and $b = -1$ and see if your answers are the same as in Q5.

2. The equation of line CD will be

   $$-\frac{1}{m}(x - a) + b \text{ or } -\frac{1}{m}x + \left(\frac{a}{m} + b\right).$$

   The coordinates of point D will be

   $$\left(\frac{a + bm}{1 + m^2}, \frac{am + bm^2}{1 + m^2}\right).$$

   The translation vector from C to D will be

   $$\left\langle\frac{bm - am^2}{1 + m^2}, \frac{am - b}{1 + m^2}\right\rangle.$$

   And point D' will be at

   $$\left(\frac{a + 2bm - am^2}{1 + m^2}, \frac{2am - b + bm^2}{1 + m^2}\right).$$

   You can check your answers just as in the previous problem.

Walking Rex: An Introduction to Vectors (page 137)

Student Audience: Algebra 1/Algebra 2

Prerequisites: None. This activity is designed to be a first introduction to vectors.

Sketchpad Proficiency: Beginner. Students work with a pre-made sketch.

Activity Time: 20–30 minutes. It may be possible to do this activity and the follow-up activity, Vector Addition and Subtraction, in one class period. We recommend using two periods, though, so that the material has more of a chance to sink in.

Required Sketch: Walk the Dog.gsp from the folder 5_Transform

Walk the Dog

Q1 The magnitude stays the same. (In other words, Rex is always the same distance—the length of his leash—from the tree.)

Q2 a. $(4.33, 2.50)$
   b. $(0, 5)$
   c. $(3.54, 3.54)$

   Note that the x-coordinate in part a and both coordinates in part c are approximations—the answers students get may be slightly different. (The exact value of the x-coordinate in part a is $2.5\sqrt{3}$ and the exact value of either coordinate in part c is $2.5\sqrt{2}$.)

Q3 a. magnitude: 5; direction: $0°$
   b. magnitude: 5; direction: $53.13°$
   c. magnitude: 5; direction: $270°$
   d. magnitude: 5; direction: $233.13°$
   Note that the direction values in parts b and d are both approximations—the answers students get may be slightly different. (The exact value for part b is $\arctan(4/3)$ and for part d it's that value plus $180°$.)

Q4 Rex should move to $(-5, 0)$ to get away from the ladybug when she's at $(5, 0)$, and $(-3, 4)$ to get away from her when she's at $(3, -4)$.

   In general, vectors (a, b) and $(-a, -b)$ face opposite directions.

Q5 The only things that change when vector j is dragged are the locations of its head and tail. The first method for defining vectors uses magnitude and direction—neither of these changes as j is dragged. The second uses the coordinates of the head *when the tail is at the origin.* Regardless of where the head and tail actually are, the coordinates of the head still *would* be the same if the tail *were* at the origin.

Q6 (82, 84). No matter where you're standing, Rex is 2 units to the right of you and 4 units "north" of you.

Q7 Walk 2: (83, 81). Drag the vector so that "you" are at the origin. Rex will be at (3, 1), meaning that he is always 3 units to the right of you and 1 unit "north" of you.

Walk 3: (74, 83). Drag the vector so that "you" are at (8, 6). Rex is at (2, 9), meaning that he is always 6 units to the left of you and 3 units "north" of you.

Q8 Walk 2: (86, 82). If the leash were twice as long, Rex would be 6 units to the right of you and 2 units "north" of you.

Walk 3: (68, 86). If the leash were twice as long, Rex would be 12 units to the left of you and 6 units "north" of you.

Vector Addition and Subtraction (page 140)

Student Audience: Algebra 1/Algebra 2

Prerequisites: Students should have completed the previous activity, Walking Rex, before doing this one.

Sketchpad Proficiency: Beginner. Students work with a pre-made sketch.

Activity Time: 20–30 minutes. It may be possible to do the previous activity, Walking Rex, and this activity in one class period. We recommend using two periods, though, so that the material has more of a chance to sink in.

Required Sketch: **Walks.gsp** from the folder 5_Transform

Sketch and Investigate

Q1 (7, 9)

Put j's tail at the origin and k's tail at j's head. The coordinates of point B, k's head, are the answer.

Q2 The answer is still (7, 9).

Q3 head: (7, 9); tail: (0, 0)

Q4 (21, 10)

Put k's tail at the origin and j's tail at k's head so that point A, whose coordinates are given, is the destination point.

Q5 (19, 9)

Put j's tail at the origin this time and k's tail at j's head so that point B, whose coordinates are given, is the destination point.

Q6 Line up the head of the first vector with the tail of the second vector. The sum is the vector from the first vector's tail to the second vector's head.

Q7 Yes, vector addition is commutative. The drawing on the first page of the activity demonstrates this: Whether you add the shorter, more vertical vector to the longer, more horizontal vector, or vice versa, you end up in the same place.

Q8 Two vectors whose sum is zero have the same magnitude but face opposite directions.

Vector Addition and Subtraction

Continued from previous page.

Q9 Vector subtraction is just like vector addition except that what is added is the *opposite* of the second vector (which we'll call the "opposite vector" here). Thus, line up the head of the first vector with the tail of the opposite vector. The difference is represented by the vector from the first vector's tail to the opposite vector's head.

Q10 No, vector subtraction isn't commutative. In fact, the difference of two vectors is the opposite of the difference taken in the reverse order.

Explore More

1. The coordinates of vector m are $(j_1 + k_1, j_2 + k_2)$. The coordinates of vector n are $(j_1 - k_1, j_2 - k_2)$.

Exploring Algebra with The Geometer's Sketchpad
© 2002 Key Curriculum Press